LEADERSHIP

to Math Success for All

NCSM–Houghton Mifflin Company
School Division and McDougal Littell
Monograph Series for Leaders in
Mathematics Education

Edna F. Bazik
Editor

Address inquiries to: NCSM, Executive Director, 6550 Vallejo St, Ste 202, Emeryville CA 94608-1112 or email to tbelcher@ncmonline.org

ISBN-13: 978-0-618-38446-4
ISBN-10: 0-618-38446-4

1 2 3 4 5 6 7 8 9—EB—16 15 14 13 12 11 10 09 08 07

Table of Contents

Introduction: Addressing the Special Needs of Students

Edna F. Bazik and Carole Greenes

With the enactment of the Education for All Handicapped Children Act *(PL94-142)* in 1975, various instructional methods and curriculum modifications were introduced into classrooms nationwide to meet the special educational needs of children, ages 3 to 21. The goals of PL94-142 were reaffirmed in the Individuals with Disabilities Education Act *(1990, 1997, and 2004)*. As IDEA points out, all students with disabilities are entitled to appropriate education designed to meet their unique needs. The importance of equity in educational opportunity for all students, not just those identified in IDEA, is the focus of the No Child Left Behind Act of 2001. NCLB resulted from concern about the great number of students failing to make adequate progress in school. NCLB holds states and their schools accountable for the educational achievement of all students.

The importance of equal opportunity for all students to learn mathematics is highlighted in NCTM's *Principles and Standards for School Mathematics* (2000). One of the six principles that must guide the teaching of mathematics is the Equity Principle. "All students regardless of gender, ethnicity, race, socio-economic status or physical challenge, must have opportunities to study—and support to learn—mathematics."

Addressing the special learning needs of all students is an enormous challenge facing mathematics teachers at all levels, Prekindergarten through grade 12. How can teachers best provide for the special needs of students in a regular education classroom? How can mathematics leaders and college educators better prepare mathematics teachers to work with students with various learning needs? How can special education teachers collaborate with regular education teachers to provide a rich program for all students? It is these questions that are addressed in this monograph. There are a variety of opinions about how to best serve students with various needs. The articles in this monograph represent the opinions of authors and are not necessarily those of the editors, NCSM, or Houghton Mifflin.

In the first article, "Measuring Number Sense Development in Young Children," Ben Clarke, Scott Baker and David Chard cite esearch in reading that shows that systems for preventing academic lifficulties are more effective for improving outcomes for struggling tudents than are remedial efforts after difficulties are discovered. They lescribe a similar approach in the mathematical education of young chil-lren in the area of number sense.

In "Ability Grouping, the Debate Goes on . . . for a Century!" Kathryn Tomasiewicz and Barbara Hinsberger consider the issue of abil-ty grouping as a means of attending to the different needs of students. As they point out, supporters view ability grouping as a way to maximize he potential of students. Opponents cite the lack of research. Who is ight?

In the next four articles, authors offer strategies for assisting students vith special needs in the classroom. In "Strategies for Enhancing English Language Learners' Success with Mathematics," Debra Coggins suggests vays to help students with limited English language skills in regular education classrooms. She gives numerous examples of the use of visual ools and language supports. At the end of the article, Coggins provides ecommendations for the professional development of teachers who have ELLs in their classrooms.

Melfried Olson, Judith Olson, Mary Swarthout, and Kim Hartweg lescribe a learning station approach to meet the needs of special stu-lents in inclusive classrooms. In "Meeting Special Needs in Mathematics Through Learning Stations," they not only present the goals and benefits of the stations, but they also address strategies for educating teachers in he use of this approach.

In "Methods and Strategies to Help All Students Be Successful in Secondary Mathematics," Larry Bradsby describes an alternative teaching approach that has the potential of maximizing learning for all students. He highlights the importance of identifying outcomes, diagnosing stu-lent needs, establishing criteria for selecting appropriate activities, using a variety of measures to determine student achievement, and maintaining student data.

In "Technology Uses in Special Education Mathematics Class-rooms," Michael L. Connell, Richard Klein, and Delwyn Harnisch present an intervention model in which technology plays a prominent role. They stress the importance and value of carefully linking technology to the content and the pedagogical approach. Their model is illustrated with several case studies.

The final three articles focus on the preparation of teachers to work with students with special educational needs. In "Supporting

Collaborative Teaching Between Mathematics and Special Educators: What Can Supervisors Do?" Marguerite M. Mason, Sharon H. deFur, and Virginia L. McLaughlin describe collaborative partnerships, their benefits, and their challenges. The authors also provide mathematics leaders with suggestions of ways to foster and support these collaborations.

Sherry Meier and Beverly Rich take on the challenge of how to prepare special education teachers to teach mathematics in their article, "Preparing Special Needs Teachers for Teaching Standards-Based Mathematics: Focusing the Curriculum." In their preparation program, Meier and Rich engage teachers in tasks that require them to examine mathematics standards, textbooks, and curricular time allocations, and reorganize and reorder the content around big ideas they typically teach.

In the final article, "Infusing Inclusive-Based Practices into Elementary School Mathematics Methods," Gary Greene and Hal Anderson describe their revised undergraduate methods course for prospective elementary school teachers that showcases ways to modify curricula, make instructional accommodations, and analyze case studies. They point out that separate courses in special education and mathematics education are not as successful as an integrated approach to preparing mathematics teachers to work in inclusive classrooms.

We hope that taken together these articles provide you with insights into and strategies for enhancing the instruction of students with special educational needs.

On behalf of the National Council of Supervisors of Mathematics, we thank our distinguished authors who contributed their knowledge, expertise, and time in preparing articles for this important monograph. To Edna Bazik, our guest editor, we express our deepest gratitude for recruiting the distinguished authors, reviewing the manuscripts, and quickly responding to all requests for additional information. We offer major thanks to our wonderful NCSM editor, Janet Pittock, for her careful review and recommendations and for preparing the manuscript for printing; to NCSM members and others who served as reviewers of the articles; and to the outstanding editors and designers at Houghton Mifflin for their help in producing this monograph. Finally, all of us in NCSM are most grateful to Houghton Mifflin for their financial support of the publication and distribution of the monograph series, and for their ongoing support of leadership in mathematics education.

Measuring Number Sense Development in Young Children: A Summary of Early Research

Ben Clarke, Scott K. Baker, and David J. Chard

Introduction

Preventing academic difficulties, rather than remediating them once they have become pronounced, is receiving increased attention in both general and special education. Prevention is perceived as a way to more effectively address differential instructional needs among students, efficiently allocate precious educational resources, and seriously address the achievement gap among students. Remediating established academic problems is based on a wait-to-fail approach, which is harmful to students, not supported by research, and increasingly difficult and expensive to implement as students get older. A prevention approach is based on the premise that intense instruction and support should be provided to children before they experience prolonged failure and before there is a discrepancy between their academic performance and the performance of their peers. This presumes, of course, that children who would otherwise experience academic difficulties can be reliably identified early before they begin experiencing difficulties.

Preventing academic difficulties, rather than remediating them once they have become pronounced, is receiving increased attention.

Once at-risk students are identified, research-based instructional practices can be provided so that the gap in achievement does not have an opportunity to develop in the first place, or if there is a small gap, it can be reduced relatively easily. Recent research suggests that systems for preventing academic difficulties hold much more promise for improving outcomes for struggling students than maintaining the current wait-to-fail approach *(Vaughn & Fuchs, 2003)*.

Several research studies suggest that a prevention model is likely to be effective for improving the literacy outcomes for students at risk for reading difficulties while reducing the number of referrals to special education *(Good, Kame'enui, Simmons, & Chard, 2002; Vaughn, Linan-Thompson, & Hickman, 2003)*. One such prevention model is the three-tier model, a school-wide approach to providing literacy instruction. The first tier represents a strong, evidence-based instructional model designed to prevent difficulties in reading. The second tier is instruction designed to meet the needs of about 15% of the student population who are not developing literacy skills as expected based on assessments that are sensitive to growth on important early literacy skills. This instruction is typically provided in small groups, supplements the first-tier instruction, is briskly paced, and is flexible to allow students to receive this support only as long as they need it. The third tier is instruction that is individualized to meet the needs of students who are significantly behind their grade-level peers in literacy development. This instruction is aligned with the literacy expectations and standards but may require a significantly slower pace of introduction, the extensive use of scaffolds, and a significant amount of time spent on review *(Walker et al., 1996)*.

Fuchs and Fuchs *(2003)* contend that a model of preventing mathematics difficulties could be constructed that is similar to the three-tier model for preventing reading difficulties. This model would comprise a process of screening and implementation of appropriate instructional practices to prevent mathematical difficulties before they occur. Any attempt to identify students at-risk for later mathematics failure would need to determine which early mathematics skills could form the basis of an early identification assessment system. Previous research in the area of mathematics learning disabilities (MLD) offers some insights into key early indicators of mathematics difficulty.

Any attempt to identify students at-risk for later mathematics failure would need to determine which early mathematics skills could form the basis of an early identification assessment system.

The incidence of MLD has been estimated to be 5 to 8 percent of the school age population *(Geary, 2004)*. One noted characteristic of students with MLD is intact but delayed skills in basic numerical competencies such as Arabic numeral identification and magnitude comparison *(Geary, Bow-Thomas, & Yao, 1992)*. Thus a potential measure of early mathematics might be designed to reflect a later skill that distinguishes students with MLD from their peers with no mathematics learning disability. Such a measure could also tap into a child's emerging number sense. There are a couple of reasons for examining children's understanding of early concepts of number. First, basic number concepts that children acquire in early childhood are likely to lay the foundation for the development of more advanced mathematical concepts *(Ginsburg & Allardice, 1984)*. Secondly, the success or failure to acquire early numerical concepts influences students' interest and confidence in learning mathematics and may alter their long-term success in mathematics *(Jordan, 1995)*.

For the past three years, we have conducted a series of research studies intended to support a model for preventing mathematics difficulties in the primary grades. In the sections that follow, we describe studies that focus on developing, testing, and validating measures of early number sense in kindergarten and grade 1 and the implications for teaching that would arise from use of these measures.

Overview of Research

The research conducted in our initial study examined the reliability, validity, and sensitivity of four experimental early mathematics measures designed for use in early identification and formative evaluation. The measures were based on number sense and were designed to assess the precursors of mathematics understanding acquired by children before they are able to do formal mathematics.

Participants were 52 first-grade students. In the 2000–2001 academic year, seven measures of mathematics, four experimental measures, and three criterion measures were administered to participants. The four experimental measures were *Oral Counting* (OC), *Number Identification* (NI), *Quantity Discrimination* (QD), and *Missing Number* (MN) *(Clarke & Shinn, 2004)*. The criterion measures were the *Woodcock Johnson Applied Problems subtest* (WJ-AP) *(Woodcock & Johnson, 1989)*, the *Number Knowledge Test* (NKT) *(Griffin, Case, & Siegler, 1994)*, and *Math-Curriculum Based Measurement* (M-CBM) *(Shinn, 1989)* first-grade computation probes.

Each of the experimental measures was individually administered. All were one minute in duration. Copies of the standard directions, scoring rules, and sample measures are available from the authors. The Oral Counting (OC) measure required students to orally count beginning with 1. The final score on oral counting was the greatest number counted. The Number Identification (NI) measure required participants to orally identify numbers between 0 and 20 when presented in random order with a set of printed numerals. The Quantity Discrimination (QD) measure required participants to orally state which of two visually presented numerals was greater. Numerals from 0 through 20 were randomly sampled. The Missing Number (MN) measure required participants to orally state the missing number from a string of three consecutive numbers, 0 through 20. The missing number was in the initial, the middle, or the last position. Data were collected three times during the year, in October (fall), February (winter), and May (spring), with approximately 13 weeks between data collection periods.

In the fall, participants scored highest on the Oral Counting measure (60.4) followed by the Number Identification measure (36.0), the Quantity Discrimination measure (19.2), and the Missing Number measure (11.3). The same rank order of measures from highest to lowest score occurred in the winter and spring assessments. Across all four experimental measures, participants' scores improved from fall to winter to spring, implying change over time. The greatest growth was for the OC measure, followed by the NI, QD, and MN measures, in that order.

The inter-scorer, alternate-form, and test-retest reliability of the experimental early math measures were examined at different points in the study. All measures had long-term reliability approaching or exceeding 0.80. All measures had reliability above accepted criteria for screening decisions *(Salvia & Ysseldyke, 1998)*.

Concurrent criterion validity between the experimental and criteria measures were examined for the fall with the NKT and the WJ-AP, winter with M-CBM, and spring with M-CBM and the WJ-AP data collection periods. Concurrent validity correlations were strongest for the QD measure, ranging from 0.71 to 0.88 with a median of 0.75. Of the experimental measures, the OC measure had the lowest correlations, ranging from 0.49 to 0.70 with a median of 0.60. The NI measure and MN measure concurrent validity evidence ranged from 0.60 to 0.70 with a median of 0.66 and the MN measure ranging from 0.68 to 0.75 with a median of 0.71.

Predictive validity data were analyzed between the fall experimental measures and M-CBM collected in the winter and the WJ-AP and M-CBM data collected in the spring. Predictive validity was also assessed between the winter experimental measures and the WJ-AP and M-CBM data collected in the spring. The QD measure had the highest median correlation of 0.76, followed by the MN measure (0.72). Both the NI measure (0.68) and the OC measure (0.56) had strong relationships as well.

In summary, each of the experimental measures showed preliminary evidence of reliability and both concurrent and predictive validity. However, as a starting point for the development of a measure designed for early identification and formative evaluation, evidence of reliability and validity are necessary but not sufficient. Due to the unique purposes of such measures other factors are paramount as well. The data indicated that the measures showing the greatest reliability and validity

(QD and MN) might not have as much potential use in early identification and formative evaluation because of floor effects and limited growth over time. Floor effects occur when many students have scores at the lower end of the continuum of scores, thus making it more difficult to discern which students are at-risk, and then because of limited growth, harder to measure their development over time. Thus, a primary question raised by this research was the need to further examine the complex role between traditional aspects of measurement development (i.e., reliability and validity) while examining score distributions and growth data to ensure that measures could be used in early identification and formative evaluation. A detailed report of this complete can be found in Clarke & Shinn *(2004)*.

In addition to further research examining what measure works best for first grade, questions were raised concerning the role of kindergarten mathematics development. Specifically, could a measurement net be designed that tracked student performance in early mathematics from kindergarten through first grade? To answer these questions, an additional study was conducted with both kindergarten and first-grade students. The purpose of our second study was to examine the efficacy of a set of potential screening measures to identify students who are likely to experience later mathematics difficulties by comparing their performances to a validated outcome measure in kindergarten and first grade.

Participants in the second study were 168 kindergarten and 207 first-grade students in seven schools in a medium-sized school district in the Pacific Northwest. Across the seven schools, the percent of students who qualified for free and reduced lunch ranged from 27% to 69%. Thirteen percent of the students in the district were minorities and approximately 4% were English language learners. In kindergarten and first grade, 4% and 12.6% of the students, respectively, were on IEPs.

Participants were administered a set of seven experimental measures and one criterion measure three times during the 2002–2003 academic year (fall, winter, and spring) with approximately 16 weeks between administration periods. The experimental measures were *Oral Counting* (OC), *Number Identification* (NI), *Quantity Discrimination* (QD), and *Missing Number* (MN) described in Study 1. Several variations to these measures were introduced in this study, as well. In the NI, QD, and MN measures, variations included a restricted range of numbers for kindergarten of 1–10 and a range in first grade of 1–20. OC was modified to capping student response at 20. In the QD measure in the fall, students were allowed to point or verbally respond. The MN included a measure in which the missing number was always at the end (MN-BE) and a measure where the missing number varied in its position in the number sequence (MN-BV). The criterion measure was the *Number Knowledge Test* (NKT) *(Griffin, Case, & Siegler, 1994)*. The *Number Knowledge Test* was selected because it was found to be highly correlated with a published measure of mathematics achievement, the SAT-9 *(Harcourt Educational Measurement, 1996)* in both kindergarten and first grade.

The findings of the second study suggest that the development of a measurement net to screen students for potential mathematical difficulties is attainable. We are encouraged that the measures that seem most promising in the second study are the same as those for which technical adequacy was established in the first study. Strong positive correlations between the experimental measures and the criterion measure were again obtained and the results of regression analyses indicate that the measures also accounted for a substantial amount of variance in the criterion measure. In part this addressed our purpose of establishing whether the measures predict outcomes in kindergarten and first grade. The results of the second study also raise additional questions regarding the utility of these measures for predicting longer-term outcomes on commercially published measures of mathematics achievement. A detailed report of the second study can be found in Chard, Clarke, Baker, Otterstedt, Braun, and Katz *(2005)*.

The development of a measurement net to screen students for potential mathematical difficulties is attainable.

Discussion and Conclusion

For teachers, schools, and districts utilizing the early numeracy measures described in the previous section, we believe that there are several outcomes that would ideally result. First, and from our perspective the most important, a link would be established between assessment of early mathematics skill and the instruction that occurs in the classroom and or the school. Models for linking assessment to instruction are numerous, but the three-tier model that has been advocated for and implemented successfully in beginning reading has enabled schools to collect early literacy data and use it to think about students belonging in one of three categories representing a continuum of skill level and instructional support. The categories *benchmark, strategic,* and *intensive* represent students on track and likely to be successful in the core reading curriculum, students at some risk and likely to need supplemental support, and those students at risk and needing intensive support to meet critical literacy outcomes.

Schools implementing a three-tier model in reading have thus been able to provide a range of instructional support and services matched to student need. Thus far, a similar three-tier model has not been developed for mathematics with students in kindergarten and first grade. The development and use of early numeracy measures in a school or classroom would enable instructional leaders to match the level of instructional support to the level of student need in mathematics. For many schools that have previously approached early mathematics instruction with a one-size-fits-all approach, the ability to differentiate instruction based on student skill level would have the effect of profoundly altering how mathematics instruction is thought about and more importantly how it is delivered to all students in a school or a teacher's classroom.

The development and use of early numeracy measures in a school or classroom would enable instructional leaders to match the level of instructional support to the level of student need in mathematics.

Although the three-tier model holds similarities across reading and mathematics assessment and instruction, a number of differences do exist. Most pronounced is the paucity of research into the development of early mathematics. The breadth of research on beginning reading development and the resulting synthesis of this knowledge base has allowed schools to focus instruction on the critical areas or big ideas of phonological awareness, alphabetic principle, accuracy and fluency with connected text, vocabulary, and comprehension. If early literacy assessments are aligned with the big ideas of beginning reading instruction, they will not only detect general categories of student skill level (i.e., benchmark, strategic, or intensive), but they can provide specific information about a student's strengths and weaknesses in relation to the five big ideas of reading instruction. A school or teacher can align instructional support based on both degree of need and specific skill area so that a student at-risk in a particular area can receive additional instructional support to enhance understanding of the concept or skill. The same student would not receive instructional support in other areas, if deficits in those areas were not detected.

In comparison, the limited research base in mathematics and corresponding lack of "big ideas" in beginning mathematics instruction means that the measures described above may create a three-tier model in early mathematics that can detect broad strokes of instructional need but may not specify exact instructional targets. The lack of such big ideas and research on core components of math instruction are in part why we do not know of any three-tier model in mathematics that is being implemented in the same fashion as the three-tier model in reading described above.

It should be noted that each of the measures was designed to assess critical mathematics content, but the exact relationship between the measures and critical instructional content is not yet known. For example, the ability to compare magnitudes or discriminate between quantities appears to be a significant development for children, taking various forms as they age, from comparing sets of objects *(Starkey, Spelke, & Gelman, 1983)* to comparing numerals *(Siegler & Robinson, 1982)*, but whether or not this skill is a critical instructional target is not yet known. However, we do know that the quantity discrimination measures developed to assess the specific ability to determine which of two visually presented numbers is greater does allow a student to utilize more sophisticated strategies for solving a range of problems that are presented to them in early mathematics. For example, a student that was able to discriminate which of two numbers was bigger in an addition problem could then employ the strategy of counting on from the larger addend rather than the less sophisticated strategy of counting all or counting on from the smaller addend. Future research on early mathematics measures should attempt to discern the preliminary skills and instructional targets that lay the foundation for children to perform successfully on math tasks presented to them at school and stay apprised of corresponding developments in research on early mathematics instruction.

It should also be noted that all of the measures we are currently using focus on a student's skill in the domain of number and do not address other areas of mathematical thinking, such as geometry. As researchers' understanding of mathematical development increases, attempts to design measures in other domains of mathematics outside of number should be undertaken.

A second major implication of our research into early mathematics assessment has been the need to focus on both a student's performance at one point in time and the child's growth in understanding over time. By contrast, in traditional mathematics assessments, greater attention is placed on a student's standing in comparison to peers. Although this provides valuable information, it does not allow the teacher or school to make judgments regarding the student's response to instruction. For teachers and schools, the ability to examine growth in mathematics provides a chance to create a robust instruction and assessment cycle where assessment occurs at frequent points during instruction and informs instructional changes to ensure student success.

The early intervention and prevention approach that has been widely adopted in the field of reading is gaining acceptance *(Snow et al., 1998)*. Although the exact connection between early performance in the domain of number sense and later math development has not yet been documented, we believe that the development of an assessment tool that can reliably identify children who are at-risk for developing mathematical difficulties upon school entry is particularly critical. The National Research Council *(2001)* reports that as early as first grade, children who are not performing successfully may lose the motivation they brought with them to school to explore and learn mathematics. The criticism of their performance can lead to a belief that they do not have the necessary ability, or just are not smart enough to succeed at math. Therefore, early identification to get these students on track at the outset is an effective way to avoid this downward spiral for students and to produce positive mathematical outcomes for all students.

The ability to examine growth in mathematics provides a chance to create a robust instruction and assessment cycle where assessment occurs at frequent points during instruction and informs instructional changes to ensure student success.

For additional information about the studies described in this paper or copies of the directions, scoring rules, and the measures, please email Dr. Clarke at clarkeb@uoregon.edu.

References

Chard, D. J., Clarke, B., Baker, S., Otterstedt, J., Braun, D., & Katz, R. (2005). Using measures of number sense to screen for difficulties in mathematics: Preliminary findings. *Assessment for Effective Intervention, 2,* 3–14.

Clarke, B., & Shinn, M. (2004). A preliminary investigation into the identification and development of early mathematics curriculum-based measurement. *School Psychology Review.*

Fuchs, L. S., & Fuchs, D. (2001). Principles for the prevention and intervention of mathematics difficulties. *Learning Disabilities Research & Practice, 16,* 85–95.

Geary, D. C. (2004). Mathematics and learning disabilities. *Journal of Learning Disabilities, 37,* 4–15.

Geary, D. C., Bow-Thomas, C. C., & Yao, Y. (1992). Counting knowledge and skill in cognitive addition: A comparison of normal and mathematically disabled children. *Journal of Experimental Child Psychology, 54,* 372–391.

Ginsburg, H. P., & Allardice, B. S. (1984). Children's difficulties with school mathematics. In B. Rogoff and J. Lave (Eds.), *Everyday cognition: Its development in social context* (pp. 194–215). Cambridge, MA: Harvard University Press.

Good, R. H., Kame'enui, E. J., Simmons, D. C., & Chard, D. J. (2002). *Using dynamic indicators of basic early literacy skills in a school-wide model for primary, secondary, and tertiary prevention.* Unpublished manuscript. Eugene: University of Oregon.

Griffin, S. A., Case, R., & Siegler, R. (1994). Rightstart: Providing the central conceptual prerequisites for first formal learning of arithmetic to students at risk for school failure. In K. McGilly (Ed.), *Classroom lessons: Integrating cognitive theory and classroom practice* (pp. 25–49). Cambridge, MA: MIT Press.

Harcourt Educational Measurement (1996). Stanford Achievement Test Series, Ninth Ed. San Antonio, TX: Harcourt Educational Measurement.

Jordan, N. D. (1995). Clinical assessment of early mathematics disabilities: Adding up the research findings. *Learning Disabilities Research & Practice, 10,* 59–69.

National Research Council (2001). *Adding it up: Helping children learn mathematics.* J. Kilpatrick, J. Swafford, and B. Findell (Eds.). Mathematics Learning Study Committee, Center for Education, Division of Behavioral and Social Sciences and Education. Washington, DC: National Academy Press.

Salvia, J., & Ysseldyke, J. (1998). *Assessment in remedial and special education* (5th Ed.). Boston: Houghton Mifflin.

Siegler, R. S., & Robinson, M. (1982). The development of numerical understandings. In H. W. Reese & L. P. Lipsitt (Eds.), *Advances in Child Development and Behavior, 16,* (pp. 241–311). New York: Academic Press.

Shinn, M. R. (1989). *Curriculum-based measurement: Assessing special children.* New York, NY: The Guilford Press.

Snow, C., Burns, M. S., & Griffin, P. (Eds.), (1998). *Preventing reading difficulties in young children.* Washington, DC: National Academy Press.

Starkey, P., Spelke, E. S., & Gelman, R. (1983). Detection of intermodal numerical correspondences by human infants. *Science, 22* (4620), 179–181.

Vaughn, S., & Fuchs, L. (2003). Redefining learning disabilities as inadequate response to instruction: The promise and potential problems. *Learning Disabilities Research and Practice, 18,* 137–146.

Vaughn, S., Linan-Thompson, S., & Hickman, P. (2003). Response to instruction as a means of identifying students with reading/learning disabilities. *Exceptional Children, 69,* 391–409.

Walker, H. M., Horner, R. H., Sugai, G., Bullis, M., Sprague, J. R., Bricker, D., & Kaufman, M. J. (1996). Integrated approaches to preventing antisocial behavior patterns among school-age children and youth. *Journal of Emotional and Behavioral Disorders, 4,* 194–209.

Woodcock & Johnson, (1989). *Woodcock Johnson Applied Problems subtest* (WJ-AP). Itasca, IL: Riverside.

Ability Grouping, the Debate Goes on . . . for a Century!

Kathryn Hehl Tomasiewicz and Barbara Smolenski Hinsberger

Introduction

Many issues in education lend themselves to fierce debate. In the United States one of the most divisive has been the issue of ability grouping. Supporters of ability grouping view it as a necessary and desirable means through which individuals can maximize their potential. Opponents, driven by social conscience, maintain there is no evidence that ability grouping benefits any students at any level, but is in fact a practice by which students, due to gender, social class, or race, are restricted in their education and thereby limited in life choices. The argument becomes one of excellence versus equity. Ironically the two diametrically opposed sides cannot see their common ground, the educational benefit for children.

Defining Ability Grouping

Although many countries practice ability grouping, the United States has the longest tradition of grouping at the primary level. Heavily influenced by psychological theories prevalent at the turn of the twentieth century and the intelligence testing movement, which took hold after World War I, the United States emphasized individual differences, innate abilities, and pedagogical practices that resulted in homogeneous groupings of students according to their competencies, particularly in language arts and mathematics *(Arnove & Zimmerman, 1999)*. Although the practice of grouping in middle and high school began to wane by mid-century, it regained status by 1960 *(Mallery & Mallery, 1999)*.

The practice of ability grouping and the accompanying debate remain unabated with the onset of the twenty-first century. The nineties, known as the decade of "educational confusion" as a result of the reform wars, found key factions of the educational community on opposing sides. With each claiming support by research evidence, The National Council for the Social Studies opposed ability grouping, while the National Council of Teachers of Mathematics supported differentiated instruction *(Agne, 1999)*. With implementation of No Child Left Behind *(NCLB, 2001)*, the debate nears its centennial with no end in sight.

Further complicating the philosophical issues of the debate, confusion exists around the actual terms "tracking" and "ability grouping." Tracking is often used to describe any form of ability grouping *(Oakes, 1990; O'Neil, 1992)*. Although used interchangeably, the terms have different meanings and implications for implementation. Sandholtz, Ogawa, and Scribner *(2004)* identify the general term tracking as referring to two related practices—academic tracking and ability grouping. Academic tracking is the practice of placing students in classes according to achievement for the purpose of completing a prescribed sequence of classes—college-preparatory, general, or vocational. Ability grouping refers to a specific kind of tracking, in which students are invited to join different classes within a given subject area. The current trend is to replace the term ability, which infers an issue of permanence, of innate skill, with the terms achievement grouping or flexible grouping, which focus on skill-specific performance.

Working from the three types of ability grouping identified for talented individuals by Clark and Zimmerman, Arnove *(1999)* restructured them for the general student population. The first type, mixed-ability grouping, takes three forms—(1) in-class enrichment, (2) cooperative learning, and (3) individualized instruction. The second type, homogeneous ability grouping, can take four forms—(1) specialized schools, (2) specialized classes in regular school for full days, (3) special grouping for part of the school day, and (4) special grouping for school-related activities. The final type of grouping is acceleration or retention, which also takes multiple forms—(1) grade skipping, (2) early admission, and (3) repeating a grade.

With these practices in widespread use in our educational system, it begs the question, "What does the research show?" With each side declaring support from research evidence, a brief summary of the research is cited below.

Summarizing Research on the Effects of Heterogeneous Grouping

The argument for heterogeneous grouping centers on political correctness and educational equality through equal access to education. Standards-based reform exemplifies the effort to depart from a differentiated curriculum and create more intellectually demanding content and pedagogy, thereby improving the quality of education for all students *(Cohen, 1996; O'Day & Smith, 1993; Rowan, 1996)*.

Heterogeneous grouping allows all students to have greater exposure to the best teachers who, in a more traditional model, generally receive assignments for advanced classes. These teachers have been found to invest more time in preparing to teach, offer better instruction, spend more time on instructional activities over lecture methods, and include more variation in learning tasks *(Oakes, 1985)*. Their instruction typically utilizes higher-level thinking skills such as analysis, critical thinking, and problem solving that are then incorporated into the assessment component. Exposure to this type of instruction and assessment over rote memorization and basic skills better prepares students for college entrance examinations and the opportunity to continue their education.

Several psychological concerns are also circumvented by exposure to better teachers. Research shows that students perform in relation to teacher expectations, regardless of ability levels *(Dickens, 1996; Evans, 1995; Finn, 1972)*. Placement in heterogeneous grouping raises teacher expectations, which prevents lower motivation and achievement prevalent in low-ability groups. It also prevents students from being relegated to a lower status in the academic hierarchy. Such identification typically results in less respect from peers *(Hallihan & Oakes, 1994)* and often results in lower self-esteem and an increased dropout rate.

Research shows that students perform in relation to teacher expectations, regardless of ability levels.

Furthermore, heterogeneous grouping prevents a disproportionate number of racial and ethnic minorities from being placed into low-ability groups, which tend to remain constant throughout their educational experience. As such, the practice of heterogeneous grouping offers the best legal approach to dismantling ability grouping as a denial of equal educational opportunity along racial lines *(Dickens, 1996)*.

Finally, heterogeneous grouping challenges the 70-year-old concept of placement in an educational track based on innate ability or IQ. Heterogeneous grouping replaces traditional intelligence tracking with alternative possibilities such as cooperative grouping whereby each team member can bring his or her unique talent to the task or grouping.

On a systemic level, tracking contributes to mediocre schooling for most students. It exaggerates, rather than reduces, initial differences in student ability and performance. Rather than equalizing educational opportunity, academic tracking and ability grouping tend to produce inequitable outcomes that fail to increase overall student achievement *(Sandholtz, Ogawa, & Scribner, 2004)*.

On a systemic level, tracking contributes to mediocre schooling for most students. It exaggerates, rather than reduces, initial differences in student ability and performance.

Summarizing Research on the Effects of Homogeneous Grouping

Homogeneous grouping is the practice of grouping students with similar ability levels for subject matter instruction. Without homogeneous grouping, differentiation becomes an enormous task for the classroom teacher, and the individual instructional needs of all levels of students may not be met. Appropriate curricula for each ability level should also be provided so that children have the best chance of mastering the material. Students at each level of readiness should have the chance to be engaged in work that is meaningful and focused on specific learning needs *(Kulik, 1992)*.

Without homogeneous grouping, differentiation becomes an enormous task for the classroom teacher, and the individual instructional needs of all levels of students may not be met.

Early in their educational programs, students recognize that they have different interests, talents, and academic strengths. Those differences should not be overlooked; rather, they should be built upon. Students feel good about their progress if instruction is focused at their level of readiness, but students do not all learn the same way, at the same pace, with the same materials, and with identical outcomes. Low-performing students do not necessarily model the behavior of more able students, and mixing groups should not be done for the sake of the learning model *(Shunk, 1987)*. The self-esteem of lower-ability students

Low-performing students do not necessarily model the behavior of more able students, and mixing groups should not be done for the sake of the learning model.

may actually be higher when placed with similar children because they feel free to ask questions of the teacher and others without fear of appearing "dumb." Interestingly, the self-concept of the more able student has been shown to be slightly lower at first when grouped together because they are amid peers with the same high ability. However, studies show that this usually evens out after a short period of time *(Kulik, 1993)*.

The use of ability or achievement grouping is more widely used in subjects where skill development is necessary to move forward. Reading complex literature is dependent on a good foundation of the basics of word decoding and comprehension. Studying algebra is dependent on a good foundation of the basics of number sense and problem solving as well as computation. However, grouping should be flexible. Students should not be required to remain at a level in the face of overwhelming frustration, nor should they be discouraged from challenging themselves to higher expectations.

If all children are to extract the most benefit from instruction, they must be taught at their appropriate levels and be exposed to higher-level thinking skills. Lower levels should not focus on memorization and simple recitation of facts. Problem solving and critical thinking skills must be integral to all levels and not be reserved for the high-ability students.

Problem solving and critical thinking skills must be integral to all levels and not be reserved for the high ability students.

Finally, variables such as class size and available resources have to be kept equal for any type of grouping to be successful. Because this has not often been the case, much of the research citing poor results for grouping is invalid because without control of these variables, researchers have not been able to test the effectiveness of low-ability classes. If support services and better funding were available, groupings of low-performing students would see more success *(Maddox & Wheelock, 1995)*.

Conclusion

With each side of the debate citing research evidence, can both sides be right? Much of the cynicism about educational research lies in the fact that the majority of the existing research on the effects of grouping is 25 years old and little of it has been done controlling the variables of 1) differences in student abilities, 2) teachers' attitudes and techniques, and 3) curriculum variation in topic and rigor that occurs when comparing classes for grouping research. However, when quality data have been collected from studies that control for these variables, evidence consistently shows that all students benefit from within-class grouping, especially in mathematics.

Agne *(1999)* provides a good summary of the research on ability grouping. She cites a meta-analysis conducted by Robert Slavin, an opponent of tracking, and James Kulik, a proponent of some tracking and ability grouping. Both found that ability or achievement grouping, both within classes and across grades in elementary settings, afforded more achievement for all groups involved, whether low, average, or high.

Though divided on many aspects, research shows that some form of temporary ability grouping, based on a specific aptitude in a skill or content, when complemented by appropriate instruction, may have significant effects on student achievement *(Tieso, 2003)*, and math classes of all ability levels achieve more in tracked classes.

No Child Left Behind *(2001)* and the reauthorized Individuals with Disabilities Education Improvement Act of 2004 *(IDEA)*, with its Response to Intervention model are forcing educators to be aware of, address, and monitor the academic gains of all students. Driven by this legislation, attempts to improve and equalize student achievement have resulted in standards-based curricula. However, while attempting to level the playing field through the establishment of demanding content and pedagogy for all students, standards-based curricula have created the evolution of "standard gaps." Because of concerns over equity in grouping raised by Jeannie Oakes *(1985)* in her research, these curricula are being imposed on an educational environment that has seen a decrease in specialized programs for children labeled as gifted and talented as well as those identified as needing extra assistance. Ironically, education finds itself still fully embroiled in the debate as it struggles with the need for differentiated curricula and instruction aligned with students' academic achievement.

Research shows that some form of temporary ability grouping, based on a specific aptitude in a skill or content, when complemented by appropriate instruction, may have significant effects on student achievement.

Ability grouping practices must take care not to repeat earlier practices. As educators, we must move beyond the concept of one's ability

We must embrace the concept of flexible grouping and continually respond to the child's performance through progress monitoring.

and purposefully focus on achievement and performance of specific skills. There is no longer support for a fixed system that does not allow for specific content to be studied, or motivation, past accomplishments, or present potential of the student to be considered. We must embrace the concept of flexible grouping and continually respond to the child's performance through progress monitoring.

To argue that separating children by achievement levels denies them equity in education assumes that the classroom is much like a bus—if students have equal access to a seat in the classroom, equity has been served *(Grossen, 1996)*. Equity in education is more. Equity is served when the growth rates of children starting at the low achievement levels match or exceed the growth rates of children starting at the high achievement levels *(Grossen, 1996)*. The critical variables have more to do with instruction than with grouping.

As the courts have already ruled, the question is not whether a school groups by ability or not; the question is how well the low performers do. If these low-achieving students are not learning as well as they could, equity is not being served, regardless of the grouping arrangement *(Grossen, 1996)*. One can only caution that equity is an important element of education but not if it comes at the expense of groups of students who lie at the high or low end of the normal curve.

References and Bibliography

Agne, Karen (1999). Kill the baby: Making all things equal. *Educational Horizons, 77*(3), 140–147.

Arnove, Robert F. & Zimmerman, Enid (1999). Dynamic tensions in ability grouping: A comparative perspective and critical analysis. *Educational Horizons, 77*(3), 120–127.

Brewer, D., Rees, D., & Argys, L. (1995). Detracking America's schools: The reform without cost? *Phi Delta Kappan, 77*(3), 210–215.

Cohen, D. K. (1996). Standards-based school reform. Policy, practice and performance. In Haymore, Ogawa, & Scribner, Standards gaps:

Unintended consequences of local standards-based reform. *Teachers College Record, 106*(6), 177–202.

Dickens, A. (1996). Revisiting Brown v. Board of Education: How tracking has resegregated America's public schools. In Mallery, J. & Mallery, J. (1999). The American legacy of ability grouping: Tracking reconsidered. *Multicultural Education, 7*(1), 13–15.

Evans, C. (1995). Access, equity, and intelligence: Another look at tracking. In Mallery, J. & Mallery, J. (1999). The American legacy of ability grouping: Tracking reconsidered. *Multicultural Education, 7*(1), 13–15.

Finn, J. D. (1972). Expectations and the educational environment. In Mallery, J. & Mallery, J. (1999). The American legacy of ability grouping: Tracking reconsidered. *Multicultural Education, 7*(1), 13–15.

Gallicchio, Bertile C. (1992). Tracking again: Bringing the center into focus. *English Journal, 81*(6), 75–76.

Gamoran, Adam (1992). Synthesis of research: Is ability grouping equitable? *Educational Leadership, 50*(2), 11–17.

Grossen, Bonnie (1996). How should we group to achieve excellence with equity? *Opinion paper.* National Center to Improve the Tools of Educators, Eugene, OR.

Hallihan, Maureen T. & Oakes, Jeannie (1994). Tracking: From theory to practice—Comment/reply. *Sociology of Education, 67*(2), 79–91.

Individuals with Disabilities Education Improvement Act, 2004.

Kulik, J. A. (1982). Effects of ability grouping on secondary school students: A meta-analysis of evaluation findings. *American Educational Research Journal, 19*(3), 414–428.

Kulik, J. A. (1992). An analysis of the research on ability grouping: Historical and contemporary perspectives. Storrs, CT: National Research Center on the Gifted and Talented.

Kulik, James A. (1993). An analysis of the research on ability grouping.

Kulik, James A. (2003). Grouping, tracking, & de-tracking: conclusions from experimental, correlational and ethnographic research. *Can Unlike Students Learn Together?* 1–33.

Maddox, R. & Wheelock, A. (1995). Untracking and students' futures: Closing gaps between aspirations and expectations. *Phi Delta Kappan, 7*, 222–228.

Mallery, James L. & Mallery, Janet G. (1999). The American legacy of ability grouping: Tracking reconsidered. *Multicultural Education, 7*(1), 13–15.

Marsh, H. W. & Parker, N. (1985). Self-concepts: Their relationship to age, sex and academic measures. *American Educational Research Journal, 22*(3), 422–444.

Marsh, R. S. & Raywid, M. A. (1994). How to make detracking work. *Phi Delta Kappan, 7*, 222–228.

No Child Left Behind Act, 2002.

Oakes, J. (1985). Keeping track: How schools structure inequality. New Haven, CT. Yale University Press.

Oakes, J. (1990). Multiplying inequalities: The effects of race, social class, and tracking on opportunities to learn mathematics and science. In Grossen, Bonnie (1996). How should we group to achieve excellence with equity? *Opinion paper.* National Center to Improve the Tools of Educators, Eugene, OR.

Oakes, J. (1995). Two cities' tracking and within-school segregation. *Teachers College Record, 96*, 681–690.

O'Day, M.S. & Smith, M.S. (1993) Systemic reform and educational opportunity. In Haymore, Ogawa, and Scribner, Standards gaps: Unintended consequences of local standards-based reform. *Teachers College Record, 106*(6), 1177–202.

O'Neil, John. (1992). On tracking and individual differences: A conversation with Jeannie Oakes. *Educational Leadership, 50*(2).

Rowan, B. (1996). Standards as incentives for instructional reform. In Haymore, Ogawa, and Scribner, Standards gaps: Unintended consequences of local standards-based reform. *Teachers College Record, 106*(6), 1177–202.

Sandholz, Judith Haymore, Ogawa, Rodney T., & Scribner, Samantha Paredes (2004). Standards Gaps: Unintended consequences of local standards-based reform. *Teachers College Record, 106*(6), 1177–202.

Shunk, D. H. (1987). Peer models and children's behavioral change. *Review of Educational Research, 52*(2), 149–174.

Tieso, Carol L. (2003). Ability grouping is not just tracking anymore. *Roeper Review, 26*(1), 29–36.

VanTassel-Baska, J. (1992). Educational decision making on acceleration and ability grouping. *Gifted Child Quarterly,* National Association for Gifted Children, Spring, *36*(2), 68–72.

Strategies for Enhancing English Language Learners' Success with Mathematics

Debra Coggins

Introduction

An increasing number of students in the process of learning English are enrolled in mathematics classes taught by teachers with limited training of ways to meet their needs. What preparation do these teachers need to meet the needs of English Language Learners? There is a growing body of literature outlining strategies for addressing the needs of the special students in mathematics classes *(Echeverria & Short, 2004; Chamot & O'Malley, 1994, Coggins, Kravin, Coates, & Carroll, 2007)*. In this article, three major strategies are described and suggestions made for helping teachers implement the strategies.

This article introduces three global strategies that are essential for supporting the learning of English Language Learners in the mathematics classroom—Creating and Maintaining Access to Lessons, Using Visual Tools, and Providing Language Support. The strategies are couched in terms that teachers are likely to view as reasonable and that do not call for extreme changes in teaching practice. At the same time, the strategies offer potential not only for greater learning by all students, but also for professional growth by teachers. In the course of making specific plans to incorporate the strategies into practice, a teacher is likely to more closely identify goals for lessons and to make specific plans towards those goals, to increase awareness of students' understanding and misconceptions during lessons, and through practice with visual tools, to expand personal understanding of important school mathematics.

Creating and Maintaining Access

Creating Access

Teachers must become aware of the importance of setting up learning environments where students feel safe to take risks in using their emerging academic English skills, accept challenges, and learn from their errors. The first few minutes of a lesson, sometimes referred to as the opening, the launch, or the hook, can determine whether the remainder of the class is productive for an English Language Learner.

Teachers must become aware of the importance of setting up learning environments where students feel safe to take risks in using their emerging academic English skills, accept challenges, and learn from their errors.

In the opening of a lesson on new ideas, instruction should begin by drawing students' attention to related concepts, skills, and situations that they already understand. These connections facilitate exploration and retention of the new content. The opening might include a class conversation or experience with a related cultural context, or a discussion of a problem that involves a foundational skill or concept. For example, before teaching the process for computing the product of two fractions, teachers might talk about cutting a cake, or another rectangular food item from a culture represented by students in the class. Likewise, paper folding, an activity familiar to many students, can be used to provide reinforcement of fraction ideas.

English Language Learners also benefit from established schedules and routines, including an initial announcement of what topic will be studied, what students will do, and how they will be grouped during a lesson. This forms a type of context for subsequent instruction and conversation. Naturally, English Language Learners benefit from being in visual contact with teachers who speak relatively slowly and who simplify their speech by reducing the use of idioms and highly complex sentence structures.

English Language Learners benefit from being in visual contact with teachers who speak relatively slowly and who simplify their speech by reducing the use of idioms and highly complex sentence structures.

Maintaining Access

Scaffolding learning in mathematics should help students maintain access to the lesson "without reducing the complexity of the task at hand or specifying exactly how to proceed" *(National Research Council, 2001)*. Scaffolding can take a variety of forms, including the use of simplified sentence structures in problem-solving tasks and instructions, the posing of focus questions to highlight key ideas, the provision of visual aids, and the pairing of students to consider and respond to problems.

Cooperative group and partner work can provide scaffolding if groups are facilitated in a manner that supports equity, respect, and serious effort among all group members. In a group, students can talk about their ideas, listen to ideas from other students, and ask questions. An added benefit of cooperative group work in which students collaborate and build on one another's ideas is that more challenging and interesting problems can be investigated.

Access to mathematics is maintained when teachers allow students to use alternative ways to demonstrate their understanding. For example, an annotated graph might replace a written explanation for a problem solution. Teachers must also frequently check students for understanding, and provide students with a system or method for requesting additional clarification and assistance when needed. The use of simple hand gestures for "I understand," "I understand some but not all," and "I don't get it" is one method of letting teachers know who may need more help. Visual means of supporting learning are described more fully in the next section.

Access to mathematics is maintained when teachers allow students to use alternative ways to demonstrate their understanding.

Teachers can practice creating and maintaining access by working in pairs to articulate the specific topic and goals of a lesson, methods of scaffolding and assessing understanding, and methods of clarifying new information *(Coggins, Kravin, Coates, & Carroll, 2007)*. They can cooperatively plan, present, and debrief opening explanations and activities. Access can be maintained when teachers anticipate student struggles and plan supportive questions to pose, orchestrate opportunities for student-to-student collaboration, and create formative assessment activities.

Implications for Teacher Leaders

The preceding discussion has several implications for the work of teacher leaders. Although the list is not exhaustive, it does provide a way for leaders to begin their work. Teacher leaders should do the following.

- Assist teachers in establishing classroom routines and signals, and in creating effective cooperative groups.
- Encourage teachers to collaborate and practice creating initial access for a lesson.
- Prompt teachers to gain experience in modifying written instructions and problem statements in standard textbook

lessons to make them more accessible, and to discuss ways of helping students read written instructions and problems.

- Lead teacher discussions about written or videotaped cases that offer contexts for critiquing techniques used to create and maintain access.
- Discuss links to the NCTM Equity Principle *(NCTM, 2000).*

Using Visual Tools

Marzano *(2001)* points out that assisting students in generating nonlinguistic representations for new knowledge aids thinking, communication, and recall. As students compare and contrast representations and solution methods, their conceptual understanding is enhanced *(National Research Council, 2001).* Visual tools provide an alternative means of demonstrating understanding and communicating with classmates and teachers.

Visual tools provide an alternative means of demonstrating understanding and communicating with classmates and teachers.

In mathematics classes, a wide variety of visual tools support the learning of second-language learners. Among these are pictures, objects, chalkboard drawings with accompanying text, multi-purpose graphic organizers, posters, manipulative materials, and mathematical diagrams.

Mathematical diagrams are useful visual tools because they can be used to replace or supplement wordy oral explanations. Diagrams are structural representations of mathematical relationships in which surface details, including context, are not important. As a consequence, diagrams can illuminate connections between seemingly dissimilar problems and support communication about concepts. Mendieta *(2005)* emphasizes the importance of having students translate among pictorial representations, thereby deepening their conceptual understanding.

In Japan and Singapore, mathematics instructional materials use diagrams extensively. One such diagram is the bar model. Bar models are used multiplicative, part-whole, and proportional relationships, and multi-step problem situations. They help students identify the given information in a problem and recognize the operations needed to solve the problem.

Providing Language Support

Since mathematics uses universal symbols, educators for many years believed that second-language learners would be able to learn mathematics without depending on the English language. That is no longer the case. The NCTM Process Standards *(NCTM, 2000)* emphasize the importance of oral and written communication in mathematics classrooms as a way of deepening students' understanding. As a consequence, it is extremely important that English Language Learners be provided with frequent opportunities to listen and speak about mathematics, even if they are not yet able to verbally respond to higher-level mathematical questions *(Khisty, 2004)*.

It is extremely important that English Language Learners be provided with frequent opportunities to listen and speak about mathematics.

Cooperative group work is a practical way of expanding the number of opportunities that students have to engage in productive conversations about mathematics. While working with a partner or within a small group, English Language Learners may feel more inclined to test out their ideas and express themselves in the "new" language. They also may find opportunities to speak in their native language with partners in order to clarify instructions or expand their emerging ideas. Moschkovich *(in press)* points out that mixed language use is not harmful and allows English Language Learners to get their message across.

Students with limited English language skills should not be assumed to have only basic capacity for learning mathematics. All students can benefit from listening to, and thinking about, a wide variety of questions. During whole-class discussions, teachers should ask questions that require varied levels of mathematical understanding and varied levels of oral response. Finally, teachers should thoughtfully decide which students should respond to each question.

Students with limited English language skills should not be assumed to have only basic capacity for learning mathematics.

Practical Ways to Provide Language Supports in a Mathematics Class

Simple modifications to lessons can often facilitate learning by English Language Learners. One such modification is the use of sentence starters that provide stems for student responses, as for example: "I think my answer is correct because . . ." or "I have a question about why . . ."

Another method to support language is for teachers to model problem solving by thinking aloud. This modeling will exhibit the nature of the process used in the solution and the mathematical language that is appropriate for the context. Students can then be called upon to think aloud as they solve problems.

Understanding of specific mathematical vocabulary is enhanced by purposeful instruction. Teaching new vocabulary during a mathematics lesson is usually not the same as teaching new vocabulary during a language arts lesson. A new mathematics word or phrase is highly likely to stand for a whole new, unknown concept and not be simply a context word. Thus, a foundation needs to be established before a new word can be productively introduced. Rather than beginning a lesson by trying to explain a mathematical term, an initial lesson introduction that describes the lesson goal in simple terms would be most effective. In the case of students who learned specific concepts and skills in their native language, it is important for teachers to connect, if possible, the English vocabulary to the existing knowledge.

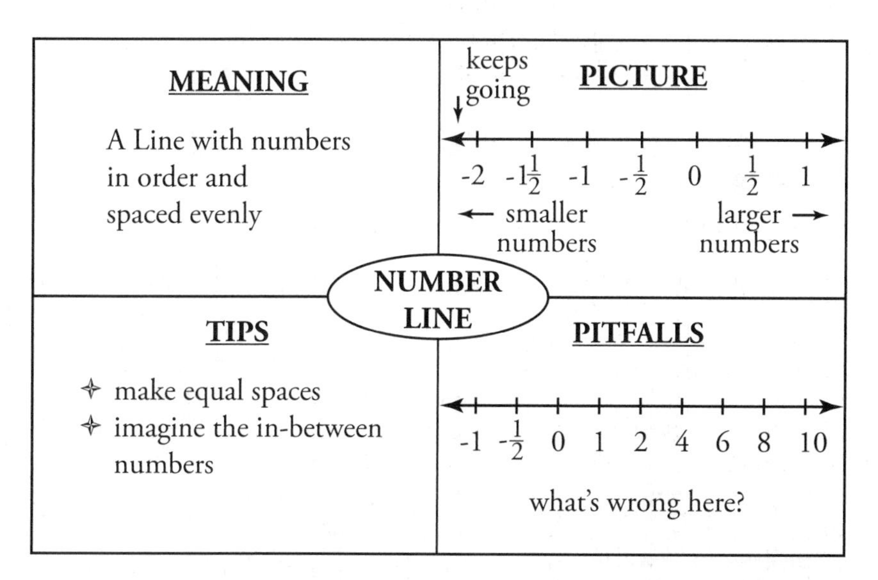

Figure 1 Figure Reprinted with permission from *English Language Learners in the Mathematics Classroom,* by Coggins, Kravin, Coates, and Carroll, Corwin Press.

Word walls and student glossaries that visibly display important mathematics vocabulary with related concepts, representations, and problems have become popular in schools across the country. Some teachers are now collaborating with their students to create word posters. Posted graphic organizers, when created as a class activity, serve as reminders of new concepts and skills, and also of related language. Figure 1 shows a poster for number lines.

Posted graphic organizers, when created as a class activity, serve as reminders of new concepts and skills, and also of related language.

Learning the Language of Mathematics

All learners, but particularly English Language Learners, benefit from purposeful instruction in understanding mathematical symbols. Rubenstein and Thompson *(2001)* outline three areas of knowledge: *reading*, or understanding the concepts represented by the symbols; *verbalizing*, or translating symbols into spoken language; and *writing* symbols, or producing symbols to represent a mathematical relationship. Students of various levels of language fluency can develop meaning for symbols through data-gathering activities as simple as making packages of eight items each, and charting the total for various numbers of packages. Letters are gradually introduced to stand for varying quantities, and symbols for operations, such as multiplication, are discussed in terms such as "3 groups of 4."

The Importance of Challenging Work and Higher-Level Thinking

Although intuitively it may seem logical to offer highly structured, simplified instruction to students with limited English language skills, research actually points towards the effectiveness of focusing on higher-level thinking questions and tasks, and student discussion and argument. This is in keeping with the NCTM standards for Problem Solving and Reasoning and Proof *(2000)*. It makes sense that students would have more to say and be more curious about others' ideas when intriguing, non-trivial problems and questions are encountered.

Although intuitively it may seem logical to offer highly structured, simplified instruction to students with limited English language skills, research actually points towards the effectiveness of focusing on higher-level thinking questions and tasks, and student discussion and argument.

Siegler *(2003)* highlights the importance of analytic thinking, or active thinking about the causes of events. He points out that purposeful engagement can increase students' efforts to understand why things work the way they do and promote analytic thinking and transfer. Of course, transfer is related to the ability to apply knowledge to a wide range of problems with similar mathematical structures and different surface features. It follows then, that students need experience identifying problems with common structures. Siegler also suggests encouraging analytical thinking by having students discuss why incorrect answers are incorrect and predict how another student may have arrived at a particular correct answer.

Conclusion

In the professional development of mathematics teachers, access and equity issues should be discussed, and practices that are currently common in mathematics classrooms with English Language Learners should be investigated. Teachers will benefit from professional development programs in which they examine their personal beliefs and practices, consider how to include more challenging work and higher-level thinking in their instruction, and are provided with opportunities to collaborate with peers to plan and purposefully incorporate more thinking types of questions for students to ponder. This may result in the changing of teaching practices that would benefit both English language learners as well as their native English speaking peers.

References

Chamot, A. U., & O'Malley, J. M. (1994). *The calla handbook: Implementing the cognitive academic language learning approach.* New York: Addison Wesley.

Coggins, D., Kravin, D., Coates, G. D., & Carroll, M. D. (2007). *English Language Learners in the Mathematics Classroom.* Thousand Oaks, CA: Corwin Press.

Khisty, L. L. & Morales, H., Jr. (2004.). *Discourse matters: Equity, access, and Latinos' learning mathematics.* Retrieved Sept. 5, 2006 from http://www.icme-organisers.dk/tsg25/subgroups/khisty.doc

Marzano, R. J., Norford, J.S., Paynter, D. E., Pickering, D. J., & Gaddy, B. B. (Eds.). (2001). *Handbook for Classroom Instruction That Works.* Alexandria, VA: Association for Supervision and Curriculum Development.

Mendieta Jr., G. (2005). *Pictorial mathematics: An engaging visual approach to the teaching and learning of mathematics.* Etiwanda, CA: Meaningful Learning.

Moschkovich, J. N. (in press). Using two languages when learning mathematics. *Educational Studies in Mathematics: Multilingual Mathematics Classrooms [Special issue].*

National Council of Teachers of Mathematics (2000). *Principles and Standards for Teaching Mathematics.* Reston, VA: NCTM.

National Research Council. (2001). *Adding it up: Helping children learn mathematics.* J. Kilpatrick, J. Swafford, & B. Findell (Eds.). Mathematics Learning Study Committee, Center for Education, Division of Behavioral and Social Sciences and Education. Washington, DC: National Academy Press.

Rubenstein, R. N. & Thompson, D. R. (2001). Learning mathematical symbolism: Challenges and instructional strategies. *The Mathematics Teacher, 94*(4), 265–271.

Siegler, R. (2003). Implications of cognitive science research for mathematics education. In J. Kilpatrick, W. G. Martin, & D. Schifter (Eds.), *A research companion to principles and standards for school mathematics,* (pp. 289–303). Reston, VA: National Council of Teachers of Mathematics, Inc.

Meeting Special Needs in Mathematics Through Learning Stations

Melfried Olson, Judith Olson, Mary Swarthout, and Kim Hartweg

Introduction

How the use of multiple-day learning stations can accommodate students with various special educational needs is the focus of this article. A format for a five-day rotation of learning stations in a classroom is provided along with a description of the use of learning stations for professional development. Van de Walle *(2004)* points out that the content of the mathematics curriculum does not need to change for special needs students. Instead, teachers need to understand how students learn and how to use that information to modify the mathematical instruction and provide better learning environments for their students. The learning stations approach capitalizes on the strengths of all students, and attends to the diversity of ability levels and learning styles. Learning stations also help teachers to assess students' understanding and make instructional accommodations without modifying the curricular content.

What Are Learning Stations?

Learning stations consist of carefully designed, related, or linked ideas and activities that engage students in problem solving, discovery, concept development and exploration of mathematical ideas. Each day, at each learning station, small groups of students work on activities and problems. Over a multiple-day period, the intact groups rotate until each group has completed the work at each station. Students have the opportunity to manage and direct their own learning experiences as they revisit mathematical topics through connected activities at the different stations. This approach to learning provides repeated but varied interactions with, and extensions of, mathematical content. While students are engaged in an activity at a learning station, the teacher is able to focus on assessing students' work and their thinking strategies.

Learning stations described in this article should not be confused with learning centers that are "supplements" or "add-ons" to the curriculum. Our learning stations are used to "teach" mathematical ideas that are integral to the curriculum, although the ideas may connect with other content areas. In this article we focus only on a multiple-day learning station approach for teaching students with special needs.

Goals of Learning Stations

Engaging tasks: One of the essential goals of multiple-day learning stations is to engage students in tasks aimed at specific mathematical objectives. To accomplish this, a learning station plan must be carefully prepared around the mathematical objectives and organized to be managed and maintained in a classroom environment.

Communication: Encouraging students to think, analyze, and explain their mathematical thinking is a central goal of multiple-day learning stations. The implementation of the learning station plan changes the role of the teacher from that of a "giver of knowledge" to a "facilitator of knowledge acquisition." Because the presentation of the mathematical content is varied across different stations, a teacher gains insight into the depth and breadth of students' conceptual understanding of the content. These insights enable teachers to make instructional decisions and accommodations.

Encouraging students to think, analyze, and explain their mathematical thinking is a central goal of multiple-day learning stations.

Student responsibility: A third goal of multiple-day learning stations is for students to become more responsible for their own learning. The engaging problem-solving tasks promote independent learning. Students are held responsible for organizing their learning materials, documenting their understanding, and keeping track of their progress and completed tasks.

Self-assessment: In conjunction with holding students responsible for their own learning, the fourth goal of multiple-day learning stations is self-assessment. The ability to assess their own learning and then to act on that assessment is an important skill for students to practice. This component can provide a teacher with a better understanding of students' strengths and weaknesses.

In summary, the use of learning stations in the mathematics classroom gives students the chance to become self-directed, to gain control over their learning, and to take pride in their achievements.

The use of learning stations in the mathematics classroom gives students the chance to become self-directed, to gain control over their learning, and to take pride in their achievements.

Multiple-Day Learning Stations

Multiple-day learning stations are built around a unit in the curriculum and students rotate through one station each day for a specific number of days. In one arrangement, five different learning stations are set up and used for the entire 5-day school week. Four or five students are assigned to one group at the beginning of the week and that group spends their mathematical instructional time at one station each day. For example, for a unit on measurement studied in grade 4, a set of learning stations could be developed around measurement activities like those described below. Care must be taken to ensure that each learning station has sufficient depth for one class period of involvement. For individual accountability purposes, a recording sheet is suggested for each student at each station to provide a record of completion.

Station 1: **The garden plot,** at which students determine perimeters of various shapes or construct shapes with given perimeters. Students use color tiles to design plots for a garden and find the perimeters of their plots by counting. Students compare perimeters of shapes with the same area. Finally, students design a fenced-in garden in whichs ten kinds of vegetables can be planted with specific constraints, and then determine how much fencing will be needed for their garden.

Station 2: **Inch by inch,** at which students use units, standard and nonstandard, to make estimates. Students first read *Inch by Inch* by Leo Lionni *(1960)*. As a second task, students estimate and then, using paper clips or one-inch tiles, determine whether small items in a box are each longer or shorter than one inch. Third, students estimate lengths of longer items to identify those that are about five paper clips in length or longer. They confirm their estimates by using clips as measurement units. As a fourth task, have students estimate lengths, find actual measures, and record their estimates and measurements for long items—measurements that require the iteration of units. Finally, students are asked to locate items that are within a specific measurement range, such as between 10 and 15 inches (paper clips) long, or about 20 paper clips long. Students sketch the items and record their measurements.

Station 3: **Drawing with technology,** where students use Logo on a computer or Explorer Draw App on the TI-73 calculator to draw a polygon of a given perimeter, as for example, a rectangle with a perimeter of 40 turtle steps or a shape that is not a rectangle that has a perimeter of 40 steps. Although this will require some familiarity with the chosen technology, the only commands students need to use are Forward (FD), Backward (BK), Right (RT) and Left (LT), along with some understanding of degrees, or how far, to turn the turtle *(Olson, J. & Olson, M., 1990).*

Station 4: **A minute or 60 seconds,** at which students predict how many times they can repeat an action in 60 seconds, such as steps taken when running in place, hopping on one foot, or tossing a ball in the air *(AIMS, 1986).* After making their predictions, students do the actions and compare their results with their predictions. After conducting three or more trials, the students graph their data and answer a set of questions such as, How close were the data to the predicted results? Were the results of the trials identical?

Station 5: **How many pennies,** at which students estimate and then determine the number of pennies required to cover a dollar bill. Students are asked to describe their estimation strategies and then apply those strategies to figure out how many pennies will cover a five-dollar bill, a regular sheet of paper, their desktops or a tabletop, and irregular shapes. To extend their thinking, students complete other tasks such as finding or constructing regions that have a "value" of 10,000 pennies, or 1,000,000 pennies *(Olson & Easley, 1996).*

Closure Activity: Students reflect on and describe what they learned from these experiences at the measurement stations. This is a good opportunity to share the data concerning how many pennies covered the outlines of their hands and how well their predictions matched their actions in the 60-second investigation. Students might also compare their drawings of figures that have a perimeter of 40 turtle steps.

Accommodations Within the Multiple-Day Learning Station Format

Accommodations are dependent on the instructional goals, the manner in which the stations are designed, and the methods by which they are implemented. When designing stations, a teacher makes necessary adjustments in the content or strategies based on the needs of students and the plans for assessment. Teachers make choices involving the formation of groups to best serve the learning needs of children. As special needs students revisit mathematical topics at connected stations, they will have repeated interactions and extended time with the mathematical topics and content. This revisiting of mathematical content in different settings provides special needs students with more opportunities to be successful at understanding the mathematical content. Although these accommodations are designed to help students with special educational needs, they no doubt facilitate learning by other students, as well.

Accommodations are dependent on the instructional goals, the manner in which the stations are designed, and the methods by which they are implemented.

Karp and Howell *(2004)* describe four aspects of a learning environment to consider when providing for individualization for students with special needs. They are to remove specific barriers, structure the environment, incorporate more time and practice, and provide clarity. By being aware of students' strengths and weaknesses, accommodations can be made at each of the learning stations to remove roadblocks or barriers. According to Karp and Howell, some of these barriers may be associated with visual or verbal/auditory memory, self-regulation, visual processing, language processing, oral or written communication, or motor skills. Learning stations provide a natural setting for making these accommodations. For example, multiple methods for presenting information such as tape-recorded directions and visual or graphic formats, can be used to assist students with auditory or visual processing deficits.

Visual images and shorter sentences in the tasks in the learning stations make directions more accessible to English Language Learners. Although clear and explicit directions are essential to the implementation of learning stations, Loven, Kyger, and Allsopp *(2004)* warn that providing clear directions and expectations does not mean telling students how to do the mathematics, but rather gives them a way to understand what is expected and a way to monitor their progress as they work through the tasks involved in the stations.

Visual images and shorter sentences in the tasks in the learning stations make directions more accessible to English Language Learners.

Efforts should be made to structure the environment so that the stations have the fewest distractions possible and that visual information is purposeful rather than overstimulating. Students with attention problems benefit from a variety of opportunities to move and be physically engaged in activities, but may have difficulty with time management and transitions. Learning stations limit the opportunities for getting "off task" by providing activities with clear purposes and expectations while concurrently maintaining the openness of the mathematical tasks to challenge and encourage all students to take risks. The mathematics content and the needs of the students determine how open ended the tasks should be so that all students can reach some level of success.

> ***Learning stations limit the opportunities for getting "off task" by providing activities with clear purposes and expectations while concurrently maintaining the openness of the mathematical tasks to challenge and encouraging all students to take risks.***

Benefits of Multiple-Day Learning Stations for Special-Needs Students

Brodesky, Gross, McTigue, and Tierney *(2004)* point out that, in order to be effective, strategies and accommodations used with students with special needs have to be connected to specific mathematical topics, the needs of the students, and the nature of the classroom environment. Multiple-day learning stations are ideal for providing these connections because teachers have a better opportunity to observe students closely enough to become familiar with their learning needs, habits, mathematical thinking, and levels of understanding. At learning stations, teachers use their skills to observe and identify problem areas, probe students' understanding in order to clarify their thinking, encourage further learning, provide feedback, and reinforce desired behaviors. Students' progress toward achieving the mathematical objectives can be better assessed and future lessons can be planned accordingly.

In summary, multiple-day learning stations can be beneficial for all students and help students with special needs in the following ways.

- Differentiation in learning can be provided for thorough engagement in different types of activities.

- Multiple assessment opportunities give students a variety of ways to represent and demonstrate their learning.
- Opportunities are provided to practice communication skills, both oral and written, in small groups.
- Passive learners are given an opportunity to work in a small group where they can't remain "anonymous."
- Students can build and expand their levels of conceptual knowledge.
- Students have opportunities for physical movement in a structured environment.
- Students working in groups are expected to ensure that all students understand expectations for each station.
- Working on a focused task with clear expectations helps students with attention deficits.
- All students achieve some level of success by working on well-chosen and planned open-ended tasks.
- Students observe and experience problem-solving strategies used by other members of the group.
- Individual differences in content knowledge and learning styles are accommodated by a variety of opportunities for student learning.

Preparing Multiple-Day Learning Stations

The teacher is responsible for finding five quality mathematical tasks that center around a mathematical goal or theme. Each of these five tasks will form the basis for one day of work for a group of children. The mathematical rationale behind each station is of utmost importance and should be identified. Although the structure will vary according to the purposes set by the teacher, we

The multiple-day format provides a nice blend of activities that provide for multiple learning styles and maximum opportunities for adaptations for students with special educational needs.

have found that the multiple-day format provide a nice blend of activities that provide for multiple learning styles and maximum opportunities for adaptations for students with special educational needs. So that students can reflect and self-assess, these learning stations should be investigative and problem solving in nature and thus, drill and practice activities are not suggested for any part of the learning station activities.

For choosing mathematical objectives and planning learning activities for multiple-day learning stations, the following format has been successful.

- Station title
- Mathematics topic(s) to be studied
- Rationale for the learning stations
- Overall goal/purpose/learner outcomes (For example, in Illinois the Illinois Learning Standards and Benchmarks were used.)
- NCTM process standards addressed
- Materials and equipment needs
- Amount of time to be spent at each station. If a learning station has several components, teachers plan the approximate amount of time needed for each component.
- Expected student actions, learning and possible probing questions for each station.
- Alternatives for special needs learners. These adaptations depend on the specific needs of the learner.
- Assessment processes. How will student learning at each station be assessed? For example, a teacher might use an observational checklist or collect student recording sheets from each station.
- A description of the closure activity. A plan to "tie-up" the learning stations at the end of the week should be designed. The plan should involve all students.

The following is an implementation plan for a one-week rotation. Over the course of a week, each child will engage in the activities at each station.

Day	*Group 1*	*Group 2*	*Group 3*	*Group 4*	*Group 5*
1	Station 1	Station 2	Station 3	Station 4	Station 5
2	Station 5	Station 1	Station 2	Station 3	Station 4
3	Station 4	Station 5	Station 1	Station 2	Station 3
4	Station 3	Station 4	Station 5	Station 1	Station 2
5	Station 2	Station 3	Station 4	Station 5	Station 1

Day 1: Introduce the stations. Place students in five groups and assign each group to a learning station for the day. Students will stay in the same group all week or the time allocated for the five rotations.

Day 2: Second rotation. Students stay in the same group and rotate to a new learning station as designated. A clearly defined posting of the rotation will provide students with guidance so that they go immediately to their stations for the day and begin their work.

Day 3: Third rotation. Groups rotate to a new station as directed by the teacher.

Day 4: Fourth rotation. Groups rotate to a new station as directed by the teacher.

Day 5: Fifth rotation and closure activity. Groups rotate to the remaining stations they have not completed. It is desirable to have a whole-class closure activity on the content and processes investigated at the stations during the week. Additional time should be designated for this discussion at the end of the week.

It may be useful to have a catch-up period or day for students who miss class or are not able to complete an activity. A day during the week or the following week could be used for whole-class discussion if that would seem appropriate for the topic and the activities.

Using Learning Stations for Professional Development

We have been involved with numerous professional development experiences involving multiple-day learning stations that have included teachers at the pre-service and in-service levels. Teachers from grades 1 through high school have successfully developed and used the multiple-day learning station model for exploration of various content areas of mathematics. Although it might initially seem like a great amount of work, the opportunity to take notes and make adjustments for future use more than makes up for the initial time spent in preparation. The benefit of this is greatly enhanced when several teachers meet together to plan and use the stations, debrief what the students learned from the stations, and make modifications for the next use of the learning stations. Our experience indicates that collaborative planning among teachers, even at different schools, has increased the effectiveness of implementation. Learning communities or lesson study groups may emerge around the development, implementation, and debriefing of a set of multiple-day learning stations.

Collaborative planning among teachers, even at different schools, has increased the effectiveness of implementation.

One of the authors has used the process of creating multiple-day learning stations as a central part of an externally funded professional development project focusing on mathematics teaching and learning for English Language Learners. This seven-day experience engaged teachers in designing a set of five learning stations with careful thought given to how to adapt and accommodate second language learners. The project focused teacher attention on *who* they were teaching (English Language Learners), *what* they were teaching (specific content objectives from state expectations), and *how* they were teaching (teacher-constructed multiple-day learning stations). The project leaders worked with teachers to improve their understanding in each area. As teachers gained information about the impact of lack of language proficiency on student learning, helpful modifications began to appear in the teacher directions created for each station. For example, in designing an interactive PowerPoint™ targeting basic place-value concepts, the teacher included instructions in both English and Spanish. Teachers began to consider written directions carefully and they streamlined the language to allow access to the posed mathematical task without diluting the expectations or the content being explored. A closer consideration of the choice of vocabulary used within the task and

Teachers began to consider written directions carefully and they streamlined the language to allow access to the posed mathematical task without diluting the expectations or the content being explored.

choosing to have dictionaries and other references such as "word walls" available to students were seen in the teacher-created work.

As they began implementing their multiple-day learning stations, teachers began to think carefully about the importance of grouping in working with English Language Learners. Choices in grouping students allowed the teacher to target individual student strengths and encourage individual responsibility for learning. After implementing the use of stations in her fourth-grade classroom, one teacher from the project commented on the power of having the flexibility to better observe and monitor students and gain valuable information about the mathematics students know by concentrating on a single station. This professional development experience, where teachers learned how to connect the who, what, and how for their learners and classrooms, allowed teachers to better prepare for teaching of mathematics to students with language needs.

Summary

We have described multiple-day learning stations as a vehicle that can be used for accommodating students of special needs. Issues such as removing barriers, structuring the environment, and providing more time and practice can be addressed by multiple-day learning stations. This approach to learning maintains high expectations for all students and is associated with numerous benefits for special needs students.

References

AIMS Education Foundation (1986). *Hardhatting in a Geo-World.* Fresno, CA.

Karp, K. & Howell, P. (2004). Building Responsibility for Learning in Students with Special Needs. *Teaching Children Mathematics, 11*(3), 118–126.

Lionni, Leo (1960). *Inch by Inch*, Astor-Honor, New York.

Olson, J. & Olson, M. (1990). "Investigations with Logo," *Projects to Enrich School Mathematics: Level I,* National Council of Teachers of Mathematics.

Olson, M. & Easley, B. (1996). "Plentiful Penny Project to Ponder"—Math by the Month, *Teaching Children Mathematics, 3*(4), 184–185.

Van de Walle, J. (2004). *Elementary and Middle School Mathematics—Teaching Developmentally*—5th edition. Pearson Education, Inc. Boston, MA.

Methods and Strategies to Help At-Risk Students Be Successful in Secondary Mathematics

Larry Bradsby

Introduction

In the past few decades there have been significant changes in the mathematics classroom at all levels. At the secondary level, there are increased requirements for graduation. All students are now required to take first-year algebra and most continue with the follow-up course, Algebra II/Advanced Algebra. Many students struggle with both the content and the curriculum approach. Students with disabilities face an even greater challenge because of difficulties they experience in acquiring and retaining knowledge *(Miller & Mercer, 1997)*.

In this article, an alternative approach to teaching mathematics that will maximize success for the students who are at risk of failure in secondary mathematics is presented. Among the topics addressed are a systematic model for instruction, a sequence of instructional activities, and a support/training program to assist teachers in the implementation of these activities.

A Systematic Model for Instruction

Studies report that 75–90 percent of mathematics classroom instruction is based on textbooks. In most cases, those books define the scope and sequence of the topics to be taught *(Tyson & Woodward, 1989)*. Research has demonstrated that the basal textbook approach to teaching mathematics is particularly detrimental to students who have learning difficulties. Cawley, Parmer, Yan, and Miller *(1996)* point out that, although normally achieving students learn mathematical concepts in a steady, incremental pattern, students with learning disabilities acquire skills in a broken sequence and have lower retention rates than their non-disabled peers. What is needed is a process to carefully monitor the progress of these students in order to successfully make adjustments in the curriculum and instructional practices at points of need.

More students will succeed if a few important concepts are taught to mastery, rather than the frequent practice of teaching numerous math skills briefly and superficially *(Dixon, 1994)*. A mastery type of program carefully monitors student progress and provides for interventions.

Guskey and Gates *(1986)* analyzed 27 research studies involving mastery learning. They found that achievement results in mastery learning programs were overwhelmingly positive, but varied greatly from study to study. In general, students in mastery learning programs at *all* levels showed increased gains in achievement over those in traditional instructional programs. They retained what they had learned for longer periods of time under mastery learning, both in short-term and long-term studies. They were engaged in learning for a larger portion of the time they spent in mastery learning classes, and they required decreasing amounts of corrective time over a series of instructional units. Students developed more positive attitudes about learning and about their abilities to learn. Finally, teachers who employed mastery learning procedures developed more positive attitudes toward teaching, higher expectations for students, and greater personal responsibility for learner outcomes. Remediation time spent by students and instructors significantly decreased as the students reached more advanced instructional units. Based on their findings, Guskey and Gates concluded that the rate at which students learn appears to be an alterable characteristic, and incorporating mastery learning procedures may be one way that slow learners can be helped to increase the rate at which they learn.

Teachers who employed mastery learning procedures developed more positive attitudes toward teaching, higher expectations for students, and greater personal responsibility for learner outcomes.

The systematic approach described in the next section incorporates many of the aspects of mastery learning. A major difference between this systematic approach and most learning programs is that the systematic approach activities follow a hierarchical schema. This approach is composed of the following teaching processes, to be performed in the order given.

1. Define the outcomes that constitute the course or unit.

2. Diagnose student strengths and weaknesses based on these outcomes.

3. Select appropriate activities to maximize student success.
4. Examine student performances to determine outcome proficiency levels after instruction.
5. Maintain records on each student's level of outcome proficiency.
6. Develop strategies and activities for students who need corrective instruction.

The Systematic Model for Instruction: The Six Teaching Processes

1. Define the Outcomes That Constitute the Course or Unit

Selecting and defining outcomes for instruction is not a difficult task. Since the vast majority of schools and textbook publishers adhere to the NCTM *Principles and Standards for School Mathematics (2000)* and traditional textbook topics, there is little variance in the expected outcomes for secondary mathematics courses at different levels. Regardless of whether curricular topics are integrated or stand alone, if students are expected to learn, outcomes can be written.

Outcomes can be designed to be very general (e.g., "Multiplying binomial expressions"), or can be stated with greater specificity (e.g., "The student will multiply binomial expressions having the same variable and a constant."). The test to measure these outcomes will define the parameters necessary for student success and will communicate to the teacher the level of difficulty and the prerequisite skills that will need to be taught. The outcomes help teachers focus on the concept to be taught, and clarify the types of resources necessary to facilitate student learning.

2. Diagnose Student Strengths and Weaknesses

By developing assessment instruments **before** *instruction, a more realistic level of performance will be expected for all students.*

For each outcome, the question that needs to be addressed is, "What level of student performance on this outcome demonstrates proficiency?" By developing assessment instruments *before* instruction, a more realistic level of performance will be expected for all students. The assessment instruments can consist of a variety of formats, including short answer, open-ended, multiple choice, and extended response items. Both a pre-instruction and a post-instruction assessment should be administered. These two instruments should be parallel in construction, unless a teacher wants to include a more comprehensive assessment of prerequisite skills in the pre-instruction assessment.

3. Select Activities to Maximize Student Success

Depending on the pre-instruction assessment results, activities can be selected in the areas that indicate need for improvement. The nature of these activities will be discussed in the section, Hierarchy of Teaching Activities.

4. Examine Student Performances to Determine Outcome Proficiency Levels After Instruction

See 2 above.

5. Maintain Records on Each Student's Level of Outcome Proficiency

Just as competent doctors maintain complete records to make beneficial health decisions, teachers who document information on student strengths and weaknesses use progress data for effective activity planning. The records can be very simple (e.g., Pass/Not Pass), as long as they are kept for each outcome and for each student. Student-progress documentation can be maintained in a teacher's grade book or on a separate form. The key is that the data should be documented for each *outcome*, not for each unit or chapter. Each student needs to be carefully monitored. Because the teacher has data on specific outcomes, immediate intervention techniques can be employed to correct misconceptions.

> *Teachers who document information on student strengths and weaknesses use progress data for effective activity planning.*

6. Develop Strategies and Activities for Students Who Need Corrective Instruction

Students who do not achieve mastery can receive remediation through tutoring, peer monitoring, small-group instruction, or additional homework *(Davis & Sorrell, 1995)*. There are many other avenues available, such

The goal is to help students keep up and not miss concepts that will guarantee failure if left unattended.

as computer instruction, game-playing at home, and after-school and weekend courses. The goal is to help students keep up and not miss concepts that will guarantee failure if left unattended. Because mathematics is hierarchical, students who move through the curriculum without understanding the foundational concepts and skills will continue to experience failure *(Bos & Vaughn, 1994)*.

Remediation is a process that addresses individual needs, whether accomplished individually or in groups. This is the part of systematic instruction that makes the greatest impact on student success. Traditionally, after completing a chapter or unit test, the next unit or chapter is started immediately, regardless of test outcomes. Grades are normally based on the percentage of correct responses on a test, and no individual outcomes (objective data) are collected. Under a systematic instructional program, with detailed progress reports and instruction modified to capitalize on students' talents and attend to their needs, no child will be left behind.

The Department of Secretary of Labor's Commission on Achieving Necessary Skills (SCANS) report in 1991 provides a blueprint of foundational skills necessary for success in the workplace. These include basic educational and vocational skills, thinking skills, problem-solving skills, and positive personal qualities. The research on mastery learning shows significant positive effects in each of these foundational skills. By using mastery learning programs in basic areas, the academic foundation for success in the twenty-first century can easily be reached by the majority of our student population *(Davis & Sorrell, 1995)*.

In summary, systematic instruction is not a new method; it incorporates many of the elements of mastery learning. It is based on the concept that all students can learn when provided with conditions and tools appropriate to their situations and abilities. The selection of appropriate activities is discussed in the next section.

Hierarchy of Teaching Activities

Not only is it critical to approach instruction with a systematic process, it is also critical to select and sequence activities such that learning is facilitated. In a traditional teaching model, 75 to 95 percent of the activities used are of the practice nature. A sequence for a systematic progression of instructional activities begins with concept-development activities, followed by practice activities, and concludes with enrichment activities. Problem-solving activities should be integrated into all teaching activities.

Concept-Development Activities

It is important to remember that concrete materials are beneficial at the concept-development stage for all grade levels. Research evidence that indicates that students who use concrete materials: (1) develop more precise and more comprehensive mental representations; (2) often exhibit more motivation and on-task behavior; (3) may better understand mathematical ideas; and (4) may better apply these ideas to life situations *(Harrison & Harrison, 1986)*. Albert Einstein said, "If I can't picture it, I can't understand it." *(Einstein, Mayer, & Holmes, 1996, p. 60)*. Concept-development activities require some kind of physical model to give students a "picture" of the mathematical concepts to be learned. Students with mathematics disabilities will benefit from concrete instruction *(Miles & Forcht, 1995; Miller & Mercer, 1993)*.

Concept-development activities require some kind of physical model to give students a "picture" of the mathematical concepts to be learned.

The use of concrete materials may help students better understand the meaning of symbols and equations *(Devlin, 2000; Maccini & Gagnon, 2000)*. The nature of the concrete materials used depends on the concept to be taught. Of course, different kinds of concrete materials are suited to different teaching purposes. Materials do not teach by themselves; rather, they complement and augment teacher guidance and student interactions, as well as reinforce demonstrations and explanations by both teachers and students *(Garnett, 1998)*.

A concrete example that will help students picture integer addition follows.

Adding integers can be modeled using colored plastic chips or dried white beans that have been sprayed on each side with a different color.

The addition of $+6$ and -4 can be modeled using one color as positive (○) and the other color as negative (●):

The fundamental concept in understanding how to find the sum of integers is that $+1 + (-1) = 0$. That is, ○● is zero, or a zero pair.

In this example, there are 4 zero pairs, so $+6 + (-4) = +2$

$+6$
-4

In typical secondary school instruction, only one model or discussion problem is used to introduce a new concept or skill. For students having difficulty, alternative concept development strategies are necessary. Problem solving should be part of concept-development activities whenever possible.

For example, after modeling integer addition using chips or beans, ask students to model problems requiring the subtraction of integers, such as $+6 - (-4) = ?$ This problem will require students to experiment and use the manipulatives to find a solution. Students use the fundamental concept of zero pairs. A typical solution is found by adding zero pairs so that a -4 can be "taken away:"

$+6-(-4)$

Since there is not (-4) to "take away," add zero pairs.

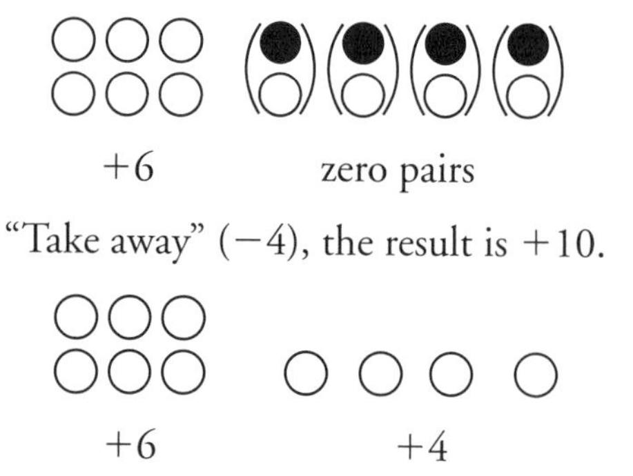

By having students explore, conjecture, and discuss possible solutions, they are involved in problem solving. Problem solving means engaging in a task for which the solution method is not known in advance *(NCTM, 2000)*. The study of mathematics is full of opportunities for students to engage in problem solving if we allow them to explore and make conjectures.

Practice Activities

Students need to practice what they are learning for several reasons.

- Practice allows students to modify, digest, and reinforce the targeted concepts.

- Practice helps with the transfer of information from short-term memory to long-term memory.

- Practice provides opportunities for careful monitoring of student progress.

- Practice allows the teacher to provide immediate corrective instruction.

It is important to provide guided practice before independent practice so that students can first understand *what* to do for each step and then understand *why* they are performing the step *(Witzel, Smith, & Brownell, 2001)*. Completing worksheets or textbook problem sets is one way to practice as well as provide feedback on student progress to the teacher. Single-concept pages without multiple concepts or mixed-problem sets work best for students with learning difficulties. Other practice activities can include games, peer-sharing and discussion, teacher-guided activities, and group projects. These types of activities create more on-task time and more student interest and enthusiasm for the topic. Again, the curriculum provided to most secondary teachers does not contain a rich variety of alternative practice strategies.

Enrichment Activities

Enrichment activities are recommended for those students who are either proficient or become proficient in the outcomes being taught and have time to explore more sophisticated mathematics. However, most secondary students who are at risk mathematically will not have time to explore these activities. The National Council of Supervisors of Mathematics (NCSM) monograph, *Activating Mathematical Talent (2003)*, addresses and offers examples of enrichment activities for mathematically talented students.

Problem-Solving Activities

Mathematics is a tool that is used to solve problems. No one makes a living by multiplying 100 facts in three minutes or by factoring a page of trinomials. These are tools that are used to solve problems. Through a variety of problem-solving activities, students should acquire ways of thinking, habits of persistence and curiosity, and confidence in unfamiliar situations that will serve them well outside the mathematics classroom *(NCTM, 2000)*. The more students are engaged in thinking situations, the more likely they will be able to address and solve new problems.

Problem solving is an integral part of all mathematics learning, so it should not be an isolated part of the mathematics program *(NCTM, 2000)*. Problem-solving activities can take many different forms and have varying levels of difficulty. Each concept being taught or physically demonstrated should employ some problem solving, whether as part of a developmental activity, a practice activity, or an independent activity. Many activities can focus on the mathematics topic being studied. For example, when studying integer addition and subtraction, give students four integers (e.g., $+3$, -3, $+8$, -8), and have them create different addition and subtraction examples using two, three, or all four of the integers. Then have students identify examples that have the same answers. Other problems can be taken from real-life applications. Most students show greater interest if the problem application has some personal meaning, as for example, being related to a job, hobby, or recent science project. Teachers need to be aware of and sensitive to situations that may lend themselves to problem-solving applications for their students.

Most states have tests that measure some degree of problem-solving ability. These test items usually propose unique problems that employ mathematics skills that students should have learned at their current or previous grade level. Any problem-solving activity, whether related to the mathematics being taught or to previously explored concepts, will help students become more agile problem solvers and better prepared for these test situations.

Teacher Support and Training of Activities

Curriculum

In a study conducted by Miller and Mercer *(1997)*, results showed that the lack of appropriate mathematics instructional materials has a detrimental effect on teaching and learning. Curricula need to be designed to facilitate a better teaching sequence that involves diagnosing student needs and selecting appropriate activities to meet those needs. Activities should be designed to address concept development, practice, and enrichment, with problem solving integrated into all activities. The activities should be carefully described so that they are readily available for teacher use without a great deal of training. Alternative strategies provide support for both teachers and students. To make it easier for teachers to plan and select strategies, a comprehensive menu of activities should be written around the outcome to be taught.

Elementary school curricula often include more learning activities and teaching strategies, as well as more supplemental instructional resources than do curricula at the secondary level. Although several models exist to teach most concepts, secondary textbooks usually employ only one model. Secondary teachers need to be supported to the same degree as elementary teachers with detailed descriptions of and instructions for using, for example, manipulative materials, computer software, and games. Teachers should not be restricted to a single-format, textbook-specific teaching approach. They need a rich set of teaching/learning resources in order to provide multifaceted, comprehensive curricular coverage.

Training

In order for teachers to implement a systematic approach of instruction, training is necessary. Most teachers have received little or no training in this area. The NCTM Teaching Principle points out that effective mathematics teaching requires understanding of what students know and need to learn, and then challenging and supporting them to learn it well *(NCTM, 2000)*. Teacher training is needed in the areas of (1) selecting and teaching to outcomes, (2) diagnosing student needs, (3) exploring alternative instructional strategies, (4) determining proficiency levels, and (5) examining corrective instructional ideas and techniques. In-service and pre-service training will be necessary to help teachers improve their teaching to meet the needs of at-risk students.

Summary

Miller and Mercer *(1997)* indicate that enough knowledge has been gathered to move mathematics educators into a "refining" rather than a "reforming" mode. Educators who remain focused on what is known to be effective practice and who refuse to be distracted by invalidated approaches will create the most successful elementary, secondary, and college programs for their students. The systematic approach to teaching will focus the data on student needs. The goal of a systems approach is success for *all* students. This is not a new method of instruction. It is based on the concept that all students can learn when provided with conditions appropriate to their situation.

Couple this approach with well-researched information on teaching strategies to maximize student success, and a stronger program can be achieved. Students need to start with concrete strategies and work toward the abstract. A variety of practice activities can keep all students more engaged. Problem solving can be integrated into all strategies to enable students to think deductively and logically. Enrichment or extensions can maximize the potential of every student. These are fundamental basic ideas to help at-risk students be successful in mathematics.

References

Bos, C. S. & Vaughn, S. (1994). *Strategies for teaching students with learning and behavior problems.* Boston: Allyn & Bacon.

Cawley, J. F., Parmer, R. S., Yan, W. E., & Miller, J. H. (1996). Arithmetic computation abilities of students with learning disabilities: Implications for instruction. *Learning Disabilities Research and Practice, 11*(4), 230–237.

Davis, D. & Sorrell, J. (1995). Mastery learning in public schools. *Educational Psychology, 3*, 702.

Devlin, K. (2000, September). Finding your inner mathematician. *The Chronicle of Higher Education,* B5.

Dixon, B. (1994). Research guidelines for selecting mathematics curriculum. *Effective School Practices, 13*(2), 47–55.

Einstein, Albert, Mayer, Jerry (compiler), & Homes, John (compiler) (1996). *Bite-size Einstein: Quotations on just about everything from the greatest mind of the twentieth century. (About Science Series.)* New York, NY: St. Martin's Press

Garnett, K. (1998). Math learning disabilities. *Learning Disabilities Research & Practice, 7*(11), 210–216.

Guskey, T. & Gates, S. (1986). Synthesis of research on the effects of mastery learning in elementary and secondary classrooms. *Educational Leadership, 43*(8), 73–80.

Maccini, P. & Gagnon, J. C. (2000). Best practices for teaching mathematics to secondary students with special needs. *Focus on Exceptional Children, 32*(5), 1–22.

Miles, D. D. & Forcht, J. P. (1995). Mathematic strategies for secondary students with learning disabilities or mathematic deficiencies: A cognitive approach. *Intervention in School and Clinic, 31*(2), 91–96.

Miller, S. P. & Mercer, C. D. (1993). Using data to learn about concrete-semi concrete-abstract instruction for students with math disabilities. *Learning Disabilities Research and Practice, 8*(2), 89–96.

Miller, S. P. & Mercer, C. D. (1997). Educational aspects of mathematics disabilities. *Journal of Learning Disabilities, 13*(3), 19–35, 61.National Council of Supervisors of Mathematics (2003). *Activating mathematical talent.* NCSM Monograph Series for Leaders in Mathematics Education, Vol. 1. Boston: Houghton Mifflin.

National Council of Teachers of Mathematics (2000). *Principles and standards for school mathematics* (2000). Reston, VA: The Author.

Secretary's Commission on Achieving Necessary Skills (SCANS) (1991). *What works with schools.* Washington, DC: U.S. Department of Labor.

Tyson, H. & Woodward, A. (1989). Why students aren't learning much from textbooks. *Educational Leadership, 47*(3), 20–30.

Witzel, B., Smith, S. W., & Brownell, M. T. (2001). How can I help students with learning disabilities in algebra? *Intervention in School & Clinic, 37*(2), 101–104.

Technology Uses in Special Education Mathematics Classrooms

Michael L. Connell, Richard Klein, and Delwyn L. Harnisch

Introduction

It has long been suggested that a closer investigation of various examples of potential uses of educational information technology in special-needs classrooms is needed *(Connell, 1989)*. Without such research it will be impossible to successfully match the strength of existing technology with the special needs of students. Lacking a conceptual framework within which to view the use of technology in the classroom, it is difficult if not impossible for effective research to be undertaken. The situation is complicated because technologies are used often on the basis of availability and rarely reflect a linkage between pedagogy, student need, and content.

In this article, we describe a unique intervention that blends conscious use of a unifying instructional model within which technology has an integral place. As such, the work reported here emerged from a tightly linked instructional system. Although sophisticated, the technology was not applied as an afterthought but fit within the same unifying pedagogical structure foundational to the entire mathematics curriculum.

To set the stage, it will be necessary to provide a brief summary of the pedagogical model used to generate the curriculum *(Connell, 2001)*. Within this conceptual framework three cases will be provided illustrating the power of the developed pedagogical and technological model. These cases will serve to illustrate some of the promises and potentials of technology usage in a special-needs classroom when a tightly linked system of curriculum and technology implementation is present.

Action on Objects

Figure 1 provides a brief overview of the instructional model used in the two cases described later in this article. When using this model it is important to remember that the instructional goal at every stage is to enable student construction of meaning as students proceed from the use of manipulatives to the level of abstraction via four transitional object types: concrete materials, sketches, mental pictures, and abstractions

(Connell, 2001; Connell, 1988)*. Within each problem type, three types of actions will typically be encountered by the student.

The instructional goal at every stage is to enable student construction of meaning as students proceed from the use of manipulatives to the level of abstraction.

1. *Memory/recall* – often of terminology;

2. *Teacher-posed problems* – related to student construction of concepts

3. *Student posed problems* – based on developing understanding of the problem space presented and its relationship to other problem types.

These activities will be experienced by the student in the form of related problems requiring the use of the developmentally appropriate object to think with—manipulatives, sketches, mental pictures, and abstractions. Furthermore, at each location in the model where a student encounters a problem—either teacher- or self-posed—the student will solve the problem via activities that are then organized and recorded for later reference.

An elementary example of this model showing actions upon all of the object types might include initial actions upon a manipulative, such as a pile of counters used to develop elementary addition. A sketch might

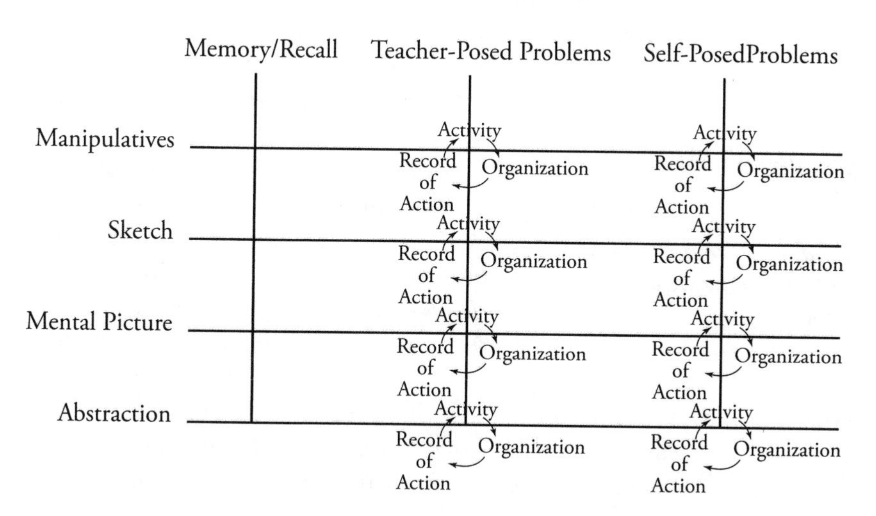

Figure 1. Action on Objects Model

then be drawn recording the actual counters, which in turn would serve as an object of thought for further construction of meaning. Mental pictures, as well as serving as another representation of the problem, provide natural entry points for technology, which will be utilized in technology-aligned classrooms. Abstraction would occur when it is no longer necessary for the student to use countable counters but when that student is capable of reflecting upon the constructed representations in the construction of new knowledge. As we thus expand our earlier notions of action upon object we can see that we are working with a carefully selected set of developmentally appropriate primitive objects and activities with these objects to build up a working vocabulary and subsequent conceptualization.

This Action on Objects model may be utilized with a parallel teaching strategy at each of the developmental levels, thus implying that the type of thinking this engenders will likewise be parallel. We would expect to see evidence of well-developed mathematical thinking at each of the stages of manipulative, sketch, mental picture, and abstraction. Furthermore, as we extend this approach, these levels may also be thought of as describing the nature of the objects that students are able to utilize in their own thinking at their current stages of development. Our task is to ensure an appropriate match between the objects with which one might think, the actions that we perform using these objects, and the answers that emerge from this process.

In doing so we were guided by the view that modern educational information technology can be used to provide "mindful engagement" that enhances students' abilities to build conceptual knowledge *(Saloman, Perkins, & Globerson, 1991)*. As experiments are performed, "instantaneous visual information," as for example, that provided by tables, graphs, simulations and animations *(Kuech & Lunetta, 2002)*, allow students to modify hypotheses and evaluate results *(Friedler, Nachmias, & Linn, 1990)*. Digital technologies have been recommended for providing real-time links between concrete experiences and their symbolic representations *(Mokros & Tinker, 1987)*, and as a consequence, offering great promise for facilitating learning by students with learning disabilities *(Maccini, Gagnon, & Hughes, 2002)*.

Modern educational information technology can be used to provide "mindful engagement" that enhances students' abilities to build conceptual knowledge.

The Cases

The three cases reported here result from a highly collaborative research project conducted at a private secondary school for students with special needs. The students attending this school have neurological differences, such as autism, Tourette's syndrome, seizure disorders, attention deficits, bipolar, and other emotional disorders that are severe enough to prohibit their attendance in public schools. Because of the wide range of diagnoses present in the students, it is necessary for teachers to implement individualized lesson plans based on each student's needs and abilities.

To accommodate this need the teaching style used throughout this project was highly learner-based and in line with Tomlinson's notions of differentiated instruction including: qualitative instruction in which the teacher tailors the work to the student's unique instructional needs, proactive instruction where the teacher is actively anticipating the instructional needs of the student and the classroom, and the ongoing use of formative assessments to modify instruction for the student *(Tomlinson, 2001)*. We were also aware of Eisner's reminder that a teacher's knowledge of individuals should be crucial in enabling them to make appropriate assignments and provide comfort and support *(Eisner, 1998)*.

Due to the level of the students and philosophical orientation of the teacher, these notions of differentiated instruction were further extended to offer the students a greater say in when they would study an objective and how fast their pace would proceed. Although the teacher maintained the final say, there was more negotiation and therefore more ownership and interest on the part of the student in regard to the learning activities. Within this approach individual lesson plans were created based upon the learning model presented here, to the extent possible.

At the time that these cases were drawn, the researcher and the school had already worked together for four years. During this period the school had adopted the learning model described in this article, and together with the research team had created supporting curricula to fit the model. Furthermore, the school was beginning a concerted effort geared toward more fully integrating technology.

During the four years leading up to these cases, the collaborative nature of the project had affected the curriculum, evaluation, and implementation at many levels. Researchers provided materials, lessons, and much of the instruction. The classroom teacher selected topics and concepts in accordance with the district and state guidelines and contributed to the instructional effort. All decision making was a team effort with the researchers and the classroom teacher working in concert.

Although technology had always played a role in the teaching and learning of mathematics at the school, this particular year was unique. Thanks to the generous contribution of a Smart Board, it was possible for the instructors to enable objects to support a Class Three Interaction in the instructional sequence *(Connell & Slough, 2005)*. At this level the technology provides a variety of feedbacks, including multiple and alternate representations to the students. The Smart Board required the use of gross motor activity for interaction. Together with the Class Three Objects supported by the Natural Library of Virtual Manipulatives (http://matti.usu.edu/nlvm/nav/), an entirely new class of actions involving large-scale body motion was required.

It is worth noting that although the research reported in this chapter utilizes the Internet website reported above, there is now a CD-based version of the interactive library of virtual manipulatives. As these three cases will show, this combination of virtual manipulatives when used in tandem with the Smart Board opened up a new world for the students concerning their explorations and learning of mathematics.

Virtual manipulatives when used in tandem with the Smart Board opened up a new world for the students concerning their explorations and learning of mathematics.

Case One

One student, whom we will refer to as Bea, has struggled with mathematics for years. Prior to the introduction of the manipulatives-enhanced Smart Board, the instructional staff had worked individually with Bea on the topic of fractions for several weeks. Traditional approaches using fraction circles, cutting fraction pieces out of paper, and using words to describe fractional parts, had met with limited success. Being eager to please, Bea would tell us "I understand," yet her tonality did not convey confidence. In what was in many ways the most telling evaluation, when asked to apply the concept to another problem, or when asked to create a problem she would like to solve, she could not do so. In particular, Bea was unable to understand the concepts upon which the mathematics was based and was unable to accurately and efficiently replicate a procedure dealing with the arithmetic at hand.

On this particular day the chief instructor opened one of the fraction tools from the virtual manipulatives library and asked Bea to "play around with the board." In a truly stellar exhibition of self-control, the instructor stepped back and watched. It was later reported that there had been a conscious decision to trust the instructional model and to let Bea learn via her own actions without intervention.

After a few hesitations and questions to the instructor that went unanswered, Bea started "playing" with the board. She turned her head sideways, shuffled her feet, and started touching the board and observing the results. In little time, Bea was able to figure out that she could change the parts in the denominator. She noticed the difference in the number of lines dividing the rectangles and noticed a color change in the lines when denominators matched. She soon recalled the multiplicative identity, applied it to solve for the values of the numerators, and successfully solved the problem. The feedback on the board told her "Good job," but she did not appear to notice the words. She already knew; her own reasoning about the results of her actions on these objects confirmed for her the correctness of her response.

It should be noted that Bea is a student who typically takes a long time to complete assignments; an average of 30 minutes to complete six basic arithmetic problems is her norm. One of the recurring comments about Bea is that she is easily distracted. However, when she was working at the Smart Board, she did not look around at her peers who where engaged in their work or socializing. She remained focused on the problem. When she had completed a few problems by herself she was smiling and obviously proud of what she had done. As Cohn suggests, the new set of cognitive strategies she had created markedly reduced her anxiety and stress in dealing with mathematics *(Cohn, 1998)*.

The new set of cognitive strategies she had created markedly reduced her anxiety and stress in dealing with mathematics.

The chief instructor reported that he was proud of the work Bea had done and decided to run an impromptu experiment. He asked Bea to show one of her other teachers what she had done in the morning in math. She went to the board and started to work on a new fraction addition problem. Her pace remained slow, and the teacher started to make suggestions to speed up the process. A careful reader will notice that this violates a central tenet of the model: that knowledge will emerge from a student's actions upon the object coupled with the object's multiple representations presented back to the student.

Although it was surprising to the other teacher, it came as no surprise to the chief instructor when Bea's movements became jittery and she immediately lost concentration. At this point the chief instructor stepped in and reminded Bea to work again with the object that she had used in solving the problem, and reminded the other teacher that she is there to observe, not intervene. Bea continued working on the problem, was able to explain most of her steps, and most importantly, was extremely pleased with the results and herself.

Case Two

Al, another student, was working well in math at the beginning of the year, but at the time this case was drawn, he was not doing much work. Al's antisocial tendency had resulted in behavior problems that landed him in the school's intensive care unit for a while. When he returned from this placement, although his behavior was much improved in terms of following directives given by the instructional staff, Al did not seem excited about his overall work; both the quality and quantity of his accomplishments had degraded significantly. Al showed very little interest in any aspect of his own learning.

This all changed one day when serendipitously the virtual manipulative library had been accidentally left on the Smart Board. Showing great interest for the first time in several months, Al asked if he could "Do that." When the teacher asked him what does "Do that" mean, Al pointed to the board and said, "Can I go up and see what that does?" This began a long and intensive interaction with the various manipulatives. Al explored a variety of problems of his own choosing. Much to the surprise of the teaching staff, he remained highly engaged for about an hour, moving ten bars around, making cubes, and exploring other features of the Smart Board. In the next class, Al was observing another student working on the same program that he had done during the previous class. Not only was Al able to interact with the Smart Board, he was also able to engage in productive interaction (a rare occurrence) with his fellow students. He provided hints to his classmates about how to move the ten bars around.

Not only was Al able to interact with the Smart Board, he was also able to engage in productive interaction (a rare occurrence) with his fellow students.

Case Three

Mark had always been interested in helping others, but rarely wanted to do his own work. Seeing this, he was assigned to help another student understand fractions and asked if they could go to the Virtual Library and choose a program dealing with fractions. They went to the Smart Board and opened up *Fraction—Parts of a Whole* (http://nlvm.usu.edu/en/nav/frames_asid_102_g_2_t_1.html). In this applet, students are asked to divide a shape into pieces of equal size by pressing the arrow buttons. Mark dominated the work and was able to show off his computer skills to his peer, giving a boost to his self-esteem.

With the next problem, Mark went to the board and started pressing the arrow button as fast as he could. His goal was to find the limit. Into how many equal size pieces could he divide the shape? "It stops at 99," he observed, "but I can do more."

When the teacher asked how Mark how he knew that he could create more than 99 equal-size pieces, he thought for a short time, looked at the board, and then moved towards a shelf with construction paper. "I can make the shapes with paper, like you did when you were working with Al." (Al was using construction paper and scissors to make halves, fourths, and eighths.)

From this start Mark worked on drawing, cutting, and gluing his pie pieces for 2 days. He soon discovered that the computer had limits—the more pieces he cut, the harder it was to keep them "equally sized." Mark returned to the board to research more about how to divide shapes into "as many pieces as possible." Subsequent to these explorations, Mark was able to apply understanding gained from working with fractions to decimals and decimal operations.

Of great interest from this case is the fluidity with which Mark was able to take the representations presented in the Class Three Object and transfer them to a physical material (paper cutting) for further investigation. The ease with which operations in the physical world were directly applicable to actions in the virtual illustrates the importance of carefully integrating the curriculum within an overarching learning model that includes technology.

The ease with which operations in the physical world were directly applicable to actions in the virtual illustrates the importance of carefully integrating the curriculum within an overarching learning model that includes technology.

Summary

In accordance with findings from previous research *(Connell, 1995)*, it was implicit in this study that technology use must be tightly linked with the instructional program. As noted by Bull *(2005)*, technology integration must be carefully planned to be effective for individuals with cognitive disabilities.

As a result of this study the following suggestions seem in order:

1) Technology should be utilized in a "tightly linked" fashion and support the underlying instructional approaches. Educational problems are not likely to be solved by merely giving students technology.

2) Technology should be used as a tool for students to use in creating their own, personally meaningful, Class Three representations. The presence of the computer alone as a delivery system of static expert representations does not guarantee, and indeed may inhibit, the development of student "re-presentations." Students should be encouraged to reference earlier representations using alternate materials to allow for further exploration possibilities and to firm up emerging understandings.

References

Bull, Prince Hycy. (2005). A case study: Technology makes a difference for people with severe cognitive disabilities. In Crawford, C., Carlsen, R., Gibson, I., McFerrin, K., Price, J., Weber, R., & Willis, D. (Eds.), *Information Technology and Teacher Education Annual,* 2005. (pp. 3902–3905). Norfolk,VA: Association for the Advancement of Computing in Education.

Cohn, P. (1998). Why does my stomach hurt? How individuals with learning disabilities can use cognitive strategies to reduce anxiety and stress at the college level. *Journal of Learning Disabilities, 31*(5), 514–516.

Connell, M. L. (2001). Actions upon objects: A metaphor for technology enhanced mathematics instruction. In D. Tooke & N. Henderson (Eds). *Using information technology in mathematics* (pp. 143–171). Binghamton, NY: Haworth Press.

Connell, M. L. (1989). Educational outcomes. In D. L. Harnisch & A. T. Fisher (Eds.), *Transition literature review: Educational, employment, and independent living outcomes,* Vol. III (pp. 55–72). Champaign, IL: The Transition Institute at Illinois.

Connell, M. L. (1988). Using microcomputers in providing referents for elementary mathematics. In M. Miller-Gerson (Ed.), *The emerging frontier: Interactive video, artificial intelligence and classroom technology* (pp. 55–60). Phoenix, AZ: Arizona State University.

Connell, M. L., & Slough, S. (2005). Technology's promise for science and mathematics learning. In Crawford, C., Carlsen, R., Gibson, I., McFerrin, K., Price, J., Weber, R., & Willis, D. (Eds.), *Information Technology and Teacher Education Annual 2005* (pp. 1910–1917). Norfolk, VA: Association for the Advancement of Computing in Education.

Eisner, E. (1998). *The kind of schools we need.* Portsmouth, NH: Heinemann.

Friedler, Y., Nachmias, R., & Linn, M. C. (1990). Learning scientific reasoning skills in microcomputer-based laboratories. *Journal of Research in Science Teaching, 27*(2), 173–191.

Kuech, R. & Lunetta, A. (2002). Using digital technologies in the science classroom to promote conceptual understanding. *Journal of Computers in Mathematics and Science Education, 21*(2): 102–126.

Maccini, P., Gagnon, J. C., & Hughes, C. A. (2002). Technology-based practices for secondary students with learning disabilities. *Learning Disability Quarterly, 25*, 247–261.

Tomlinson, C. A. (2001). *How to differentiate instruction in mixed-ability classrooms.* (2nd Ed.). Association for Supervision and Curriculum Development: Alexandria, VA.

NOTE: All websites retrieved on January 15, 2005.

Supporting Collaborative Teaching Between Mathematics and Special Educators: What Can Supervisors Do?

Marguerite M. Mason, Sharon H. deFur, and Virginia L. McLaughlin

Introduction

All educators, including mathematics educators, have been directed to leave no child behind academically. To clarify the definition, "no child" includes students with disabilities, regardless of the severity of the disability. This policy, articulated in the No Child Left Behind Act of 2001 *(NCLB)*, requires schools to demonstrate progress each year for all students. Complementing this policy is the re-authorization of special education legislation with the Individuals with Disabilities Education Improvement Act of 2004 *(IDEA)* that requires a focus on, and documentation of, instruction that leads to improving the academic achievement of students with disabilities.

Not surprisingly, the cohort of students with disabilities that take general mathematics courses and attempt to demonstrate competency on standardized tests in mathematics experiences significant challenges in meeting state standards. For example, in the Commonwealth of Virginia in 2004–05, 50% of students with disabilities passed the grade 8 mathematics standards of learning tests as compared to 86% of the non-disabled students. Furthermore, Virginia requires students to pass high school end-of-course tests as a criterion for graduation. In 2005, about 65% of the students with disabilities who took courses such as Algebra I, Algebra II, or Geometry achieved passing scores on these tests as compared to 87% of the non-disabled students.

Policy makers and educators recognize the ethical issues that underlie the need for all students to access the general curriculum. High stakes assessment in critical content areas such as mathematics holds educators accountable for the achievement of all students in those courses. The challenge becomes how to create a classroom environment that facilitates the mastery of key mathematics concepts for all students. We suggest that collaborative partnerships between mathematics educators and other general educators represent a critical element of successful classroom environments.

> *Collaborative partnerships between mathematics educators and other general educators represent a critical element of successful classroom environments.*

In this paper, we describe collaborative practices and the benefits and challenges of collaboration between mathematics and special educators. We also provide the mathematics education supervisor and special education supervisor with ideas as to how to support instructional practices that make a difference in the mathematics achievement of all students.

Collaboration and Inclusive Practices—Do They Work?

Much debate exists regarding the effectiveness of the traditional special education model of pulling students from the general education classroom for instruction. Undoubtedly, students with disabilities (and many students without disabilities) benefit from small-group intensive skill development when skills are missing or weak, but there is little evidence that ongoing removal from the general education curriculum benefits students. In fact, convincing arguments have been made based on research that students with disabilities who receive instruction primarily within the general education classroom benefit academically and socially *(Baker, 1994; Carlbert & Kavale, 1980; Rea, McLaughlin, & Walther-Thomas, 2002; Wang & Baker, 1986)*. For example, Rea et al. *(2002)* found that students in inclusive classrooms earned higher grades, achieved higher or comparable scores on standardized tests, committed no more behavioral infractions, and attended more days of schools than students served in the pull-out program.

Several other researchers find that collaborative practices such as co-teaching benefit students with and without disabilities *(Cole, 1992; Coombs-Richardson et al., 2000; Henderson, 2002; Kuglemass, 2001; Mageiera et al., 2005; Morocco & Aguilar, 2002; Wallace et al., 2002)*. Rea et al. *(2002)* stressed the importance of collaborative structures such as co-teaching and co-planning as vital to the success of the inclusive program. They identified intensive professional development in instructional and collaborative skills as being critical. Similarly, Hunt, Soto, Maeir, and Doering *(2003)* found that effective co-teaching in classrooms with students who are at risk for academic failure and students with severe disabilities raised the academic, social, and emotional success of these students.

Based on these findings, the conclusion seems apparent that collaborative practices such as co-teaching work for students with and without disabilities. Yet, there is a caveat that must be recognized when comparing the "research" to the "reality." In these research settings, the authors describe the conditions that must be in place for collaborative teaching to yield the results they observed. The reality may be that the conditions for collaboration do not exist in many schools or classrooms. Mathematics supervisors and special education supervisors have an opportunity to promote the conditions that are needed for truly effective collaborative practices to transpire.

Mathematics supervisors and special education supervisors have an opportunity to promote the conditions that are needed for truly effective collaborative practices to transpire.

What Supports Collaborative Practices in Mathematics?

Too often teachers receive a directive that they will be teaching in the "inclusion" classroom. Collaboration works best when the decision to participate is voluntary. Furthermore, this directive is seldom followed by adequate attention given to the conditions that support effective collaborative practices. The mathematics and the special education supervisors can provide leadership and model collaboration at the administrative level. Such practices communicate to the school community that mutual respect and commitment exist at the administrative level. Administrative support represents one of the key factors in the success of any instructional practice, but is particularly crucial in creating effective collaborative practices. Front-line teachers need to hear from administrators that collaborative teaching practices are valued, expected, and rewarded. Administrators must walk the talk.

Effective collaborative practices are founded upon relationships and relationships take time and work to cultivate. We also know that teachers who share similar teaching styles are often more successful in collaborative teaching settings. Mathematics and special education supervisors can provide opportunities for mathematics teachers and their special education collaborators to develop relationships in which they explore the important components of effectively working together. These opportunities should include professional development around collaboration skills and effective communication.

Paramount in any successful collaborative teaching is the opportunity for mathematics and special educators to cooperatively plan the instruction for the classroom. This co-planning time should be regular, and at a minimum occur weekly. Co-planning time provides an opportunity to review the previous instructional days and reflect and problem-solve any identified areas of concern. Teachers can identify the instructional objectives and activities and decide the role that each teacher can have in the delivery of the lessons. Teachers need opportunities to celebrate their success stories. Administrators who determine schedules and allocate resources can ensure that opportunities for co-planning occur.

Paramount in any successful collaborative teaching is the opportunity for mathematics and special educators to cooperatively plan the instruction for the classroom.

Both mathematics and special educators must believe in collaborative practices and share a commitment to making these practices work. These supervisors can facilitate this shared vision and action plan.

Educators in successful collaborative relationships gain additional personal support from their collaborators. These educators report professional growth as they learn to work together and learn from one another about their respective fields. Since all students benefit socially and academically, then, as professionals, teachers experience enhanced professional satisfaction. The classroom climate, so critical for enhanced learning, reflects the sense of achievement and efficacy in teaching. These are markers that mathematics and special education supervisors can use to measure the effectiveness of the collaborative teaching initiative.

What Challenges Collaborative Practices in Mathematics Education?

Highly qualified mathematics educators have received deep training in mathematics and possess fluent mathematical skills and conceptual understanding of their subject matter. They are granted mathematics teaching "power" based on the authority of their expertise. This authority often translates to the mathematics teacher being perceived as the "real teacher" in the classroom and an unequal status between the mathematics teacher and the special educator results. The mathematics educator may not trust the special educator with content, or the special educator may not believe himself or herself to be of value.

Likewise, highly qualified special educators may be perceived as having advanced expertise in childhood growth and development and differentiated instruction, with the mathematics educator deferring to the special educator in matters related to students with disabilities.

This knowledge disparity must be recognized by mathematics and special education supervisors as a starting point to facilitate collaboration. Special educators need to develop a deeper understanding of the content area in which they are co-teaching, and mathematics educators need to develop a deeper understanding of what is needed to reach students who have different learning needs. The assignment to co-teaching settings should not be random. Special educators who have a proclivity for, or a stronger background in mathematics, would be better choices for co-teaching in a mathematics classroom, and their interest and motivation to develop stronger mathematical skills should be supported. Cross-disciplinary training (in-service and pre-service) offers one avenue to address these challenges. The mathematics or special education supervisor can identify and support the collaboration teams by creating or sharing opportunities for professional development. This can include conferences, NCLB-supported workshops, and Mathematics-Science Partnership supported courses.

Parity between co-teachers is a critical component to the success of a collaborative mathematics classroom. Differing skills, such as described earlier, contribute to the perception of parity, but attitudes and lack of role definition may be the larger culprit. In an effective collaborative teaching environment, each teacher shares responsibility and accountability for the learning outcomes and for the day-to-day implementation of instruction. Grading, homework, lesson review, modeling, behavior management, re-teaching, demonstration, and so on, represent opportunities for role definition and the sharing of responsibility. These are explicit decisions that need to be made, but should not constitute a permanent role assignment. For example, if the special educator always has the responsibility for attendance, behavior monitoring and paper grading, then he or she may not be perceived as a true co-teacher. Lack of parity demeans the training and expertise of the special educator. On the other hand, when the special educator assumes no instructional responsibility, then the mathematics educator legitimately feels a lack of parity in the

Parity between co-teachers is a critical component to the success of a collaborative mathematics classroom.

responsibility and accountability for instruction. This situation does not serve students well. Mathematics and special education supervisors have an opportunity to observe in collaborative classrooms and identify practices that support or hinder role parity.

Consistently teachers identify a lack of time to co-plan as a barrier to effective collaborative teaching practices. One hour of co-planning per week might suffice for mature co-teaching teams, but more time is needed for teachers who are just beginning to form their collaborative teaching teams (Amerman & Fleres, 2003). Face-to-face planning is always the best, but email and phone calls also may be used to communicate and make decisions regarding instruction or the solution to problems that have arisen. Since common instructional styles influence effective collaborative practices, teachers need an opportunity to share their preferences with one another and to examine how their respective styles can complement the needs of their students. Mathematics and special education supervisors can sponsor or access training for collaborative teams that focus on instructional practices where both mathematics and special educators are developing skills at the same time.

One hour of co-planning per week might suffice for mature co-teaching teams, but more time is needed for teachers who are just beginning to form their collaborative teaching teams

What Could Collaborative Practices Between Mathematics and Special Educators Look Like?

Collaborative practices can and should vary depending on the instructional goals for the class or unit, teaching styles, developmental level of the collaborative relationship, and the classroom grouping. Recognize these factors. Mathematics and special educators need to make decisions about differing models to implement. Mathematics and special education supervisors should be knowledgeable of these collaborative teaching options so that they can observe for their effectiveness or make recommendations regarding their use.

Collaborative practices can and should vary depending on the instructional goals for the class or unit, teaching styles, developmental level of the collaborative relationship, and the classroom grouping.

Interactive team teaching, where both teachers are knowledgeable of the lesson goals and plans, offers a way to organize the collaborations.

In this model, ideally partners alternate their roles between leading instruction and supporting instruction. Until special educators acquire or demonstrate their content expertise, there may be a tendency for the mathematics educator to always be in the leader role and the special educator in the supporting role. To avoid the perception or reality of unequal roles, teams should take care to ensure that the special educator could quickly take on a leading role to maximize the communication that both teachers have value in the classroom. Homework review, test review, supporting in-class independent practice, discussion leading, and reteaching offer opportunities for instructional leadership. While the special educator is developing content expertise, he or she can contribute to the instructional team by, for example, developing student-learning profiles, adapting materials, creating learning centers, and designing supporting materials such as graphic organizers. Ideally, team teaching evolves to a point where teachers easily alternate between presenting new concepts, leading discussions, and performing other teaching roles. In this instance, the teachers have developed a high level of trust and are open to sharing teaching roles.

Station teaching offers an opportunity to provide an active learning format for students and a means of reducing the student-teacher ratio. Station teaching works best when the content has multiple activities needed to reinforce the concepts or when there are multiple instructional objectives that need guided practice and independent work. The sequence of station participation should not be an issue. In a mathematics class where there is a special educator and a mathematics educator, the content may be divided among three stations with one station for independent work (e.g., computer or lab type work), and two stations for teachers to staff. Thus in a class of 24, each station would have a group of eight students. Students can rotate among the three stations. This model allows for strategic grouping of students to ensure effective differentiation for students with varying instructional needs. Students who need enrichment can have differentiated independent station assignments that allow more in-depth exploration or expansion of the concepts while students who need additional practice can be assigned independent tasks that reinforce concepts.

Station teaching offers an opportunity to provide an active learning format for students and a means of reducing the student–teacher ratio.

Another way to achieve a reduced teacher-student ratio is to divide the class in half and each teacher deliver the lesson to the smaller mixed-skill group of students using the same lesson plan. This method is very effective when reviewing or reteaching concepts as it allows more time and opportunities for student questions and clarifications. Study guide review, standardized test practice review, or unit review can be conducted this way. This model is often referred to as *parallel teaching*. Station teaching and parallel teaching both assist students with disabilities as the reduction in teacher-student ratio provides more opportunity for direct instruction as needed.

Station teaching and parallel teaching both assist students with disabilities as the reduction in teacher-student ratio provides more opportunity for direct instruction as needed.

Some students, both those with and without disabilities, may experience difficulties with certain concepts. They may use the wrong algorithm or have a skill deficit that interferes with ongoing mastery of a concept. These students may temporarily need more intensive instruction or remediation. On the other hand, there may be a group of students (both with and without disabilities) who demonstrate a strong aptitude or interest in the mathematics concepts being explored and need guided enrichment and exploration. In these instances, one teacher (alternate the roles) works with the small group while the other teacher works with or monitors the large group. These groups may be called "flex groups" because they are flexible and not static; membership in these groups should change to avoid the label of slow or gifted. This model is sometimes referred to as *alternate* teaching.

Each of the collaborative teaching models offers opportunities to improve student learning and the classroom climate. No one model serves all instructional purposes. Mathematics and special education supervisors can help teachers choose and evaluate the collaborative teaching models they employ.

Summary

Mathematics supervisors and special education supervisors have a unique opportunity to come together and promote effective collaborative practices in schools.

In summary, you can:

- Provide administrative support and encouragement to your teachers.
- Encourage the school principal to schedule common planning time for the collaborating teachers and to maintain partnerships that are working.
- Provide the instructional resources teachers need to conduct differentiated lessons.
- Provide training for both teachers in collaboration skills, including communication, conflict resolution, and co-planning.
- Provide opportunities for both teachers to gain content and pedagogical knowledge through in-service workshops, NCLB-funded workshops, Mathematics Science Partnership–funded courses, and conferences.
- Observe teachers in collaborative teaching classrooms. Identify those teachers who are model collaborators and whose students are achieving as a result. Share these outcomes with your school administrators and the superintendent. Recognize teacher accomplishments.
- Collect data on the effectiveness of the efforts and document all aspects of the program so that you have data on which to base future decisions.
- Develop a system of rewards and recognition for collaborative initiatives. Although previous research has shown that such instruction is more effective, it is hard work that requires commitment and training. Efforts need to be rewarded.

Co-teaching can be a rewarding experience when teachers work collaboratively to meet the needs and goals of every student in the class. The Collaboration Agreement Checklist following offers an operating agreement model that collaborating teachers can adopt as they begin each year. It is important to remember that both teachers bring a unique set of abilities, skills, and talents to the classroom. The collaboration between prepared, willing teachers is invaluable for all students.

Collaboration Agreement Checklist

✓ Shared vision and goal for effective collaboration

- ○ We believe that all students can achieve in our mathematics classroom.

✓ Shared or respected teaching philosophy

- ○ We understand one another's philosophy and our philosophies are compatible if not identical.

✓ Effective teaching styles

- ○ We recognize how our teaching styles complement one another and use our individual styles to best meet the needs of our students.

✓ Supportive classroom climate

- ○ We have agreed upon classroom routines, procedures, structures, and management that promote learning.

✓ Mathematics learning is the goal

- ○ We agree that student mastery of mathematics competencies is our goal and that we will both participate in that instructional effort, learning what we need to support a differentiated classroom in math.

✓ Parity

- ○ We agree that we will both be responsible for and accountable for the instruction in this classroom; we will identify roles and share instructional responsibility on a regular basis. Both of us will be viewed as teachers of this class.

✓ Planning

- ○ We agree to use our planning time wisely to review our previous classes, plan for upcoming classes, and problem-solve learning challenges or relationship challenges. We will plan regularly and hold that time sacred.

- ✓ Instructional methods and materials
  - ○ We value one another's expertise, experience, and resources and agree to exchange ideas and materials that can benefit student learning. We agree to share the responsibility of identifying and developing materials for instruction.
- ✓ Communication
  - ○ We agree to teach and learn one another's vocabulary.
  - ○ We agree to identify ways to communicate with one another while teaching that will not interfere with the ongoing instruction and learning in the classroom.
  - ○ We agree to support one another as we learn to work together, providing constructive feedback and celebrating successes.
  - ○ We agree to be open and honest in our communication and to keep one another informed when we are not able to meet our obligations.
- ✓ Student assessment
  - ○ We agree to conduct ongoing assessment of student progress and monitor student progress to determine that our instruction is meeting student needs. We share responsibility for evaluating students and share accountability for their learning.
- ✓ Parental involvement
  - ○ We agree that parental involvement is of utmost importance in supporting student learning. We will share responsibility for parent communication and will establish a practice of informing parents of opportunities to celebrate their child's mathematics success.

References

Amerman, T., & Fleres, C. (2003). A winning combination: Collaboration in inclusion. *Academic Exchange Quarterly, 7*(3), 66–70.

Baker, E. T. (1994). *Meta-analytic evidence for non-inclusive educational practices: Does educational research support current practice for special needs students?* Philadelphia, PA: Temple University.

Carlbert, C., & Kavale, K. (1980). The efficacy of special versus regular class placement for exceptional children: A meta-analysis. *Journal of Special Education, 14,* 295–309.

Cole, C. M. (1992). *Collaboration: Research and practice. Case information dissemination packet.* Bloomington, IN: Indiana University.

Coombs-Richardson, R., Al-Juraid, S. E., & Stuker, J. D. (2000). Supporting general educators' inclusive practices in mathematics and science education, *International Consortium for Research in Science and Mathematics Education.* Costa Rica.

Henderson, K. (2002). Collaboration to benefit children with disabilities: Incentives in idea. *Journal of Educational and Psychological Consultation, 13*(4), 383(389).

Hunt, P., Soto, G., Maier, J., & Doering, K. (2003). Collaborative teaming to support students at risk and students with severe disabilities in general education classrooms. *Exceptional Children, 69*(3), 315.

Kuglemass, W. (2001). Collaboration and compromise in creating and sustaining an inclusive school. *International Journal of Inclusive Education, 5*(1), 47(19).

Mageiera, K., Smith, C., Zigmond, N., & Berbauer, K. (2005). Benefits of co-teaching in secondary mathematics classrooms. *Teaching Exceptional Children, 37*(3), 20–24.

Morocco, C. C., & Aguilar, C. M. (2002). Coteaching for content understanding: A schoolwide model. *Journal of Educational and Psychological Consultation, 13*(4), 315–333.

Rea, P. J., McLaughlin, V. L., & Walther-Thomas, C. (2002). Outcomes for students with learning disabilities in inclusive and pullout programs. *Exceptional Children, 68*(2), 203–222.

Virginia Department of Education. (2006). Virginia School Report Card. Retrieved August 1, 2005, from http://pen2.vak12ed.edu/cgi-bin/ broker?_service=doe_prod&_program=prodcode.doerp101rcdp001.sas#gr8

Wallace, T., Anderson, A. R., & Bartholomay, T. (2002). Collaboration: An element associated with the success of four inclusive high schools. *Journal of Educational and Psychological Consultation, 13*(4), 349(333).

Wang, M. C., & Baker, E. T. (1985–1986). Mainstreaming programs: Design features and effects. *The Journal of Special Education, 19*, 503–521.

Preparing Special-Needs Teachers for Teaching Standards-Based Mathematics: Focusing the Curriculum

Sherry L. Meier and Beverly S. Rich

Introduction

Traditionally United States middle school mathematics classrooms include the study of a broad range of mathematical topics every year. This allows little time to focus on in-depth understanding of any single topic. Although this type of curriculum has been criticized for decades, the "mile-wide inch-deep curriculum" is still prevalent in mathematics programs in the U.S. Unfortunately, special-needs students cannot jump from idea to idea easily and often need more time spent on important mathematical ideas in order to understand them and perform related skills.

The National Council of Teachers of Mathematics, in their *Principles and Standards for School Mathematics* (NCTM, 2000), has outlined new goals for school mathematics, including the need to develop more conceptual understanding and critical thinking or problem-solving skills. Nationally, many mathematics specialists have become familiar with these Standards and have made strides toward incorporating them into their mathematics classrooms. However, the special-needs teachers are often not mathematics specialists, and rarely have complete knowledge or understanding of these new *Standards*. As a consequence, their instructional focus remains on computation *(Maccini & Gagnon, 2000)*. Clearly, mathematics educators must raise the awareness of the NCTM *Standards* with this group of teachers, and then help them find ways to address these in a manner that is appropriate for their students.

Approximately 65% of special-needs students are categorized as either learning disabled (LD) or emotionally disabled (ED), and only 12% are enrolled in advanced high school mathematics classes. These students generally perform well below grade level, and have difficulty with basic skills, problem solving and advanced concepts *(Maccini & Gagnon, 2000)*.

Fitzmaurice *(1980)* found that special-needs teachers often were more comfortable with computational skills than with conceptual mathematical tasks; they ascribed their discomfort with concepts and tasks to their own limited background in mathematics. Perhaps this comfort level accounts in part for the fact that special-needs mathematics curricula are typically focused on computational tasks rather than on higher-order, problem-solving activities *(Heshusius, 1991)*. Recently, the No Child Left Behind legislation *(U.S. Department of Education, 2001)* has placed renewed focus on the learning of all students and equitable instruction in all strands of mathematical proficiency *(Kilpatrick, Swafford, & Findell, 2001)*. Clearly, just being able to compute is no longer adequate for any population of students.

Time Adaptations

A common adaptation made for many special-needs students relates to increased time allocated to complete assignments and tasks *(Maccini & Gagnon, 2000)*. However, increased time for completion of tasks and tests alone is not sufficient adaptation. Time for instruction should also be increased. Xin and Jitendra *(1999)* found that long-term instruction was clearly related to success when trying to promote mathematical problem solving with learning-disabled students. In general, long-term treatment was more effective in promoting both maintenance of skills and generalization of concepts than shorter-term instruction.

Long-term treatment was more effective in promoting both maintenance of skills and generalization of concepts than shorter-term instruction

Increasing time for instruction without changing the focus of the instruction is not productive either. To effectively use the increased time, it is important to focus on key mathematical ideas *(Deshler, Ellis, & Lenz, 1996)* and their applications.

Increasing time for instruction without changing the focus of the instruction is not productive.

This suggestion is the basis of the remainder of this paper. How do we help teachers of special-needs students increase the time allocations so that the students can succeed, while carefully selecting the appropriate material to stress? We need to help these teachers to focus on "big ideas" of mathematics and to identify the important mathematics within these 'big ideas." Once selected, these ideas need to be ordered in a way in which they could be appropriately taught. By reducing the number of isolated skills or ideas to teach in any school year, we can focus on developing fewer ideas, in-depth, and over an extended period of time. So, how do we help teachers develop such a curriculum?

Helping Teachers Identify and Sequence Big Ideas

Mapping Content in Texts over a Three-Year Span of Grades

One of the first things we can have teachers (or pre-service teachers) do is analyze their current curriculum, including textbooks and other instructional resources. We want teachers to consider the content presented in each grade level, with respect to various mathematical topics and how these topics are taught. With this knowledge, they can identify overlaps and gaps. To achieve this, we have assigned middle grade teachers the task of outlining one or more textbooks across the three-year span, grades 6–8. They often begin by listing titles of chapters in the textsbooks at each grade level. An example of this type of listing is shown in Table 1. Once this table is complete, teachers discuss the similarities between the various series of books for both the scope and sequence of content. They are not really surprised to see the repetitive content and sequencing from grade to grade. They often discuss their thinking about the sequential nature of the mathematics content, and their assumptions that the content is expanded upon and delved into more deeply each year. We then ask the teachers to select a specific topic that they are interested in investigating further.

Instructional Methods and Time Allocations by Content Strand over Three Years

Once teachers have selected the topic they would like to investigate further, they must perform an in-depth analysis of the content presented in each of the chapters related to that topic. Questions they must address include: How much of the content is new each year? How much is review? How much of the presentation is a repeat of the same presentation from the previous year, and how much is focused on extending or digging deeper into previously presented ideas? How much time does the teacher's edition recommend spending on each of the chapters of the

Table 1. Content by Chapter and Grade for Two Textbook Series

Topic	*Grade 6*		*Grade 7*		*Grade 8*	
	Text 1	*Text 2*	*Text 1*	*Text 2*	*Text 1*	*Text 2*
Data & Statistics	1	1	1	1	1	1
Algebra & Patterns	2	2 & 10	2 & 10	3 & 10	3, 4, & 10	2, 3, 4, & 10
Fractions	5, 6, & 7	5 & 6	3 & 4	4 & 5	7	5
Decimals	3	3 & 4	3	2		5
Geometry	8 & 11	8 & 9	5, 7, & 11	7 & 8	8 & 10	8 & 9
Measurement	4 & 11	9	5	8	8 & 9	9
Ratio & Proportions	10	7	6 & 7	6	5 & 10	6
Percent	10	7	8	6	6	7
Integers	9	10	9	3	2	2
Probability	12	11	12	9	12	11
Irrational #'s					7	5

text? For instruction? For review? For assessment? Again, the purpose is to have the teachers determine what the current practices are and what resources are provided by their current textbooks, so that we can help them move beyond their reliance on these books toward a better understanding of the important topics and ideas in mathematics.

Finally, we have the teachers take the total number of days recommended by the textbooks for instruction of specific concepts, and redistribute those days over the three years of middle school education. By doing this, teachers get a better idea of the total number of hours spent on instruction over an extended time period in a traditional classroom. Table 2 shows time allocations to fraction concepts in one middle school textbook program. The numbers of days identified for instruction, review, and assessment are those recommended in the teacher editions that accompany the student textbooks. Of particular note, of the 37 days devoted to work with fractions in the three years, 20 days are dedicated to computation with fractions. The remaining 17 pages focus on prime numbers and algorithms for finding the LCM and GCF of two numbers.

Table 2: Time Allocations for Fraction Concepts in One Middle School Program

Grade Chapter	*Topic*	*Total time allocation*	*Review and assessment recommendations*	*Instructional time allocations*
Grade 6				
Chapter 5	Number Theory (primes, LCM, GCF)	13 days	5 days	8 days
Chapter 6	Addition & Subtraction of Fractions	11 days	6 days	5 days
Chapter 7	Multiplication and Division of Fractions	11 days	5 days	6 days
Grade 7				
Chapter 3	Fraction Concepts (Primes, LCM, GCF, equivalence & comparison)	8 days	3 days	5 days
Chapter 4	Operations with fractions	11 days	5 days	6 days
Grade 8				
Chapter 7	Fractions (all concepts)	10 days	3 days	7 days
TOTALS		**64 days**	**27 days**	**37 days**

Teachers' Reactions to Their Findings

As the teachers begin to tackle these tasks, many discussions take place. Teachers often start to discuss the difference between reviewing content and reteaching the content. They generally reach consensus that reviewing means reminding the students about the meaning of terms or use of formulas and going on to new content. This is a short process, not lasting several days. By contrast, reteaching generally involves longer time periods and seeking alternate teaching strategies for presenting the same material. This typically leads to a discussion of the methods of presentation of the content from year to year in the texts, and the number of repeat activities that appear. Many teachers are surprised to find that the identical method of presentation is used in three consecutive years with no real difference in depth. They are also surprised to find that the

Many teachers are surprised to find that the identical method of presentation is used in three consecutive years with no real difference in depth.

majority of lessons and exercises presented are focused on procedures and skills, not on conceptual understanding. Teachers who work with special-needs students find this frustrating, since the textbooks don't help them present alternate strategies for reteaching, and they are focused on aspects their children often struggle with the most.

Once all information is gathered on a specific mathematical topic, we try to refocus the teachers' thinking on what happens if they change how they use this time. We ask them to think about how much more understanding could be achieved if 37 days of *instruction* on fraction concepts were spent in grade 6 and only a few days in each of grades 7 and 8. In grades 7 and 8, time could be devoted to reviewing when and how fractions are used in other contexts. Most teachers with special-needs students see this as an idea worth further investigation, but wonder how this would affect other topics. This leads to a compilation of all mathematical topics.

A summary of mathematical topics across the three grades can be compiled after all teachers have analyzed their various content topics. This generally ends up being a list of topics, similar to the unit or chapter headings from a textbook, along with time allocation recommendations. Once this list is completed, teachers compare their compilations with state or national standards. As this discussion takes place, they develop a better understanding of the standards, and how the various chapters in textbooks can fit into a fewer number of categories. For example, chapters on integers, fractions, decimals, and percent can all be seen as part of numeration and number sense. Teachers also begin to see the overlap of some topics. For example, they see measurement topics fitting into both geometry and number sense; fractions relating to measurement, probability, and statistics; and proportional reasoning relating to algebra, geometry, and number sense. In this manner, the teachers begin to understand how they can revisit specific skills within a variety of content strands or mathematical contexts, rather than treating them in isolation as unrelated skills or topics

Starting to Put the Pieces Together

This discussion often culminates in a set of "big ideas" that can be used to restructure the curriculum without reliance on textbooks, yet still include all important ideas presented in textbooks. A possible list of big ideas for middle school could be: Rational Number Sense, Proportional Reasoning, Algebraic Reasoning, Numeric Relationships and Patterns, Spatial Relationships, and Probabilistic and Statistical Reasoning. Teachers can clearly see the alignment of this set of big ideas with national and state standards. However, they now need to worry about how to sequence these ideas, and exactly what standards should be addressed within each of these big ideas.

A discussion of sequencing leads teachers to think about the mathematical understandings that are prerequisite to studying each big idea. Most teachers can easily understand and point out that students must be able to use rational numbers and fractions before addressing ideas of proportionality. They also clearly understand that number relationships and patterns should come prior to more formal algebraic reasoning. The use of fractions and percents in probability and statistics also requires that rational numbers precede instruction in formal probabilistic and statistical reasoning. Teachers also realize that proportional reasoning could come before or after spatial reasoning, depending upon when and how similarity and the use of proportions are introduced. There is generally a lot of discussion about the pros and cons of ordering the big ideas in various ways and what needs to be included in each grade level. This discussion leads teachers to a better understanding of the flexibility in the ordering of content, and also a better understanding of hierarchies they need to address.

A discussion of sequencing leads teachers to think about the mathematical understandings that are prerequisite to studying each big idea.

The Results

Using the list of middle school big ideas previously identified, one group of teachers decided on the following ordering. Rational Number Sense, Numeric Relationships and Patterns, Proportional Reasoning, Spatial Relationships, Algebraic Reasoning, Probabilistic and Statistical Reasoning. With six big ideas to be addressed across the three grades, the number of topics was reduced to two per year, allowing a great deal of time to devote to each topic.

Using this list, teachers investigate the state performance descriptors associated with each of the big ideas in the appropriate grade band, and map them into the various grade levels where they will be addressed. The teachers can attack this in groups, with each group mapping a single big idea. Table 3 (at the end of this article) shows an example of this type of mapping using the Illinois performance descriptors for middle school *(Illinois State Board of Education, 1997)*. Once these tables are combined and examined, it becomes clear to the teachers that all performance descriptors appear in the tables, and many appear multiple times. This reinforces the multiple connections among the topics, and helps the teachers feel more secure about the topics being spiraled and revisited over time.

As the teachers examine the performance descriptors for grades 6, 7, and 8, the difference in the lengths of the lists always becomes an issue. This leads to discussion about the amount of new content in each of the years, other content from grade 6 that needs to be revisited and extended (e.g., integers), and applications of previously taught concepts and skills that also compete for instructional time.

By addressing two content areas each year, teachers see how students can now focus on learning a fewer number of concepts, and learn them with understanding. The presentation of ideas is extended and connected to more situations and disciplines to help make the topic relevant to the students and allow them to explore the concepts in ways that make sense. Special needs students especially need this help in building connections and meaning.

Conclusion

This restructuring of the curriculum gives teachers and students the time they need to focus on connections and meanings needed to develop understanding and contribute to long-term retention. The process of restructuring moves teachers toward a more flexible student-based approach to instruction. At the same time it provides teachers with much needed knowledge about state and national standards, and of connections between content strands. With this knowledge, teachers can better order and present ideas in ways that capitalize on previous knowledge and skills. This multifaceted task produces an opportunity for special-needs teachers to reassess their curriculum structure, while also learning about state and national standards and improving their own knowledge of the mathematical connections and appropriate sequencing of topics.

The process of restructuring moves teachers toward a more flexible student-based approach to instruction.

Final Thoughts

The national trend toward inclusion of special-needs students the general education classrooms points to the need to consider this type of curriculum mapping on a broader scale. The same type of curriculum renewal process, discussed here, could be done for the entire student population. However, it is generally a harder sell. For special-needs students, where it is generally accepted that they need more time, this approach is not only appropriate but also needed. If we can show teachers, administrators, and parents that the approach works and students can make adequate yearly progress, then regular classroom teachers may become more interested and recognize this type of program's potential to improve all students' understanding of mathematics.

If we can show teachers, administrators and parents, that the approach works and students can make adequate yearly progress, then regular classroom teachers may become more interested and recognize this type of program's potential to improve all students' understanding of mathematics.

Table 3. Grades 6–8 Big Ideas and Related Performance Descriptors

Grade 6 Topic One: Rational Number Sense	
Introduce	Represent fractions, decimals, percentages, exponents, and scientific notation in equivalent forms.
Introduce	Select computational procedures and use them to solve practical computational problems involving whole numbers, integers, and rational numbers.
Introduce	Show evidence that computational results are correct and/or that estimates are reasonable.
Introduce	Measure length using appropriate instruments, and apply the concepts of length to practical situations.
Introduce	Test the reasonableness of findings based on data and communicate the findings.
Grade 6 Topic Two: Numeric Relationships and Patterns	
Introduce	Apply primes, factors and divisors, multiples, common factors, and common multiples in solving problems.
Introduce	Identify and apply properties of real numbers including pi, squares, and square roots.

Table 3. Grades 6–8 Big Ideas and Related Performance Descriptors (Continued)

Introduce	Apply basic properties of real numbers and order of operations to solve problems.
Introduce	Solve problems using linear expressions, equations, and inequalities.
Introduce	Apply properties of numbers to solve problems in other disciplines.
Introduce	Solve problems using multiple representations.
Introduce	Propose and solve problems using formulas and linear functions.
Introduce	Construct, develop, and communicate logical argument about numerical patterns.
Introduce	Construct, read, and interpret tables, graphs, and charts to organize and represent data.
Introduce	Compare mean, median, mode, and range with and without technology.
Grade 7 Topic One: Proportional Reasoning	
Introduce	Apply ratios and proportions to solve practical problems.
Review and Extend	Identify and apply properties of real numbers including pi, squares, and square roots.
Introduce	Solve problems using linear expressions, equations, and inequalities.
Introduce	Use graphing technology and algebraic methods to analyze and predict linear relationships and make generalizations from linear patterns.
Introduce	Apply properties of numbers to solve problems in other disciplines.
Review and Extend	Propose and solve problems using formulas, proportions, and linear functions.
Review and Extend	Solve problems using multiple representations.
Introduce	Apply properties of powers, perfect squares, and square roots.
Introduce	Apply concepts of congruency, similarity, and scale to analyze shapes found in practical applications.
Introduce	Compute distances, lengths, and measures of angles using proportions and Pythagorean theorem.
Review and Extend	Construct, read, and interpret tables, graphs, and charts to organize and represent data.

Table 3. Grades 6–8 Big Ideas and Related Performance Descriptors (Continued)

Review and Extend	Compare mean, median, mode, and range with and without technology.
Grade 7 Topic Two: Spatial Relationships	
Review and Extend	Identify and apply properties of real numbers including pi, squares, and square roots.
Review and Extend	Measure length, capacity, weight/mass, and angles using appropriate instruments, and apply the concepts to practical situations.
Review and Extend	Select and apply instruments including rulers and protractors and units of measure to the degree of accuracy required.
Introduce	Select and apply instruments including rulers and protractors and units of measure to the degree of accuracy required.
Introduce	Construct a simple scale drawing for a given situation.
Introduce	Use concrete and graphic models and appropriate formulas to find perimeters, areas, surface areas, and volumes.
Introduce	Draw or construct three-dimensional geometric figures.
Introduce	Draw transformation images of figures with and without technology.
Introduce	Use concepts of symmetry, scale, perspective, and angle measure to describe and analyze shapes.
Introduce	Identify, describe, classify, and compare two- and three-dimensional figures according to their properties.
Introduce	Construct, develop, and communicate logical arguments about geometric figures and patterns.
Introduce	Develop and solve problems using geometric relationships.
Review and Extend	Compute distances, lengths, and measures of angles using proportions and Pythagorean theorem.
Grade 8 Topic One: Algebraic Reasoning	
Review and Extend	Solve problems using linear expressions, equations, and inequalities.
Review and Extend	Use graphing technology and algebraic methods to analyze and predict linear relationships and make generalizations from linear patterns.
Introduce	Apply properties of numbers to solve problems in other disciplines.

Table 3. Grades 6–8 Big Ideas and Related Performance Descriptors (Continued)

Review and Extend	Propose and solve problems using formulas, proportions, and linear functions.
Review and Extend	Solve problems using multiple representations.
Review and Extend	Apply properties of powers, perfect squares, and square roots.
Review and Extend	Construct, develop, and communicate logical arguments about patterns.
Review and Extend	Compute distances, lengths, and measures of angles using proportions and Pythagorean theorem.
Grade 8 Topic Two: Probabilistic & Statistical Reasoning	
Introduce	Develop and solve problems using geometric models with and without technology (geometric probability).
Review and Extend	Interpret tables, graphs, and charts to organize and represent data.
Review and Extend	Compare mean, median, mode, and range with and without technology.
Introduce	Test reasonableness of an argument based on data and communicate the findings.
Introduce	Formulate questions, devise and conduct experiments or simulations, gather data, draw conclusions, and communicate results to a specific audience.
Introduce	Determine the probability and odds of events using fundamental counting principles.
Introduce	Analyze problem situations and make predictions about results.

References

Deshler, D. D., Ellis, E. S., & Lenz, B. K. (1996). *Teaching adolescents with learning disabilities: Strategies and methods.* (2nd ed., pp. 315–367). Denver, CO: Love Publishing.

Fitzmaurice, A. M. (1980). LD teachers' self-ratings on mathematics education competences. *Learning Disabilities Quarterly, 3,* 90–95.

Heshusius, L. (1991). Curriculum-based assessment and direct instruction: Critical reflections on fundamental assumptions. *Exceptional Children, 57,* 315–328.

Illinois State Board of Education (1997). *Illinois Learning Standards,* Springfield, IL: Author.

Kilpatrick, J., Swafford, J. O., & Findell, B. (Eds.) (2001). *Adding it up: Helping children learn mathematics.* Washington, DC: National Academy Press.

Maccini, P. & Gagnon, J. C. (2000). Best practices for teaching mathematics to secondary students with special needs. *Focus on Exceptional Children, 32*(5), 1–22.

National Council of Teachers of Mathematics (2000). *Principles and Standards for School Mathematics. Reston,* VA: Author.

U.S. Department of Education (2001). *No Child Left Behind.* U.S. Department of Education, Office of the Secretary.

Xin, Y. P. & Jitendra, A. K. (1999, Winter). The effects of instruction in solving mathematical word problems for students with learning problems: A meta-analysis. *The Journal of Special Education, 32*(4), 207–225.

Infusing Inclusive-Based Practices into Elementary School Mathematics Methods Courses

Gary Greene and Hal Anderson

Introduction

Three decades have passed since landmark legislation was implemented in 1975 in the form of the Education of All Handicapped Children Act *(EHA; PL 94-142)*. The EHA guaranteed a free and appropriate public education (FAPE) for all children with disabilities, regardless of the severity of their condition. Prior to this time, many children with disabilities were excluded from public schools or educated in segregated facilities without the benefit of attending neighborhood schools or interacting with peers without disabilities.

Much has changed since the implementation of the EHA. Initially, increasing numbers of public school programs became available to students with disabilities, but "mainstreaming" (i.e., including students with special needs in general education classrooms for some or all of their school day) was marginal, and students with disabilities often found themselves in separate schools or classrooms, removed from their neighborhood peers *(Smith, 2004)*. For those students with disabilities who did attend their neighborhood schools and were mainstreamed, their interaction with peers without disabilities was often limited to activities such as music, art, physical education, or as an occasional "visitor" to a general education classroom. The Individuals with Disabilities Education Act *(IDEA)* was subsequently passed in 1990, and was reauthorized in 1997, and again in the year 2004. This law has placed far greater emphasis on a fully inclusive education for students with disabilities, guided by the principle of normalization. As a result, the percentage of students with disabilities who were being included in neighborhood schools grew from 25 percent in 1985 to 96 percent by the year 2000, with more than half of the total school population of students with disabilities receiving more than 79 percent of their education in general education classrooms *(U.S. Department of Education, 2001)*.

With these data in mind, there is a clear need for general education teachers, particularly in the area of mathematics, to become knowledgeable of effective ways to modify the curriculum to accommodate students with disabilities in the classroom. Miller, Crehan, Babbit, and Pierce (2003) noted that students with disabilities have historically made poor progress in mathematics and typically perform about two grade levels below their peers without disabilities. Furthermore, mathematics difficulties that emerge in elementary school grades continue as these students progress through secondary school. These trends are likely to continue unless general education mathematics teachers improve their knowledge and skill on how to teach a more diverse student population.

This is highly challenging at the pre-service level, given the current dual system of teacher education. Wehmeyer, Field, Doren, Jones, and Mason (2004) point out that "general educators and special educators are trained and receive practices in teaching very separate, distinct types of content and types of students" and that this type of training "does not prepare teachers to meet the diverse needs of learners in schools." The authors continue by citing publications by Lesar, Benner, Habel, and Coleman (1997) and Tomlinson et al. (2002), who agree that many general educators feel unprepared work with students with disabilities. What is needed is a more unified pre-service training program for general and special education teachers in order for them to achieve shared language and philosophies, consult and collaborate, and to learn, reflect, and experiment with common practices.

With these thoughts in mind, we engaged in a full academic year process of collaboration with the intent of designing a pre-service mathematics education methods course that could meet the dual needs of general and special education teacher trainees. What follows is a description of the collaborative project, including the goals and objectives of the collaboration, course design and implementation, and pre-post data on the effects the training had on the knowledge and perceived teaching capabilities of the course participants.

Project Description

The project, supported by the College of Education at California State University, Long Beach, was a collaboration of two faculty members, one a professor of mathematics education and the other a professor of special education, the authors of this article. *Teaching Mathematics K–8 (EDEL 462)*, a three-credit course taught by the mathematics education faculty member, was the focus of the project. The course is designed to prepare pre- and in-service elementary school teachers to teach mathematics in grades K–8. The goals of the course are to (1) develop students' mathematical pedagogical content knowledge, (2) develop students' abilities to deliver mathematics instruction in an effective and efficient manner, (3) enhance students' knowledge of both the California and the National Council of Teachers of Mathematics Academic Content Standards *(2000)*, (4) enhance students' problem-solving abilities, (5) develop students' knowledge and understanding of assessment, (6) ensure that students are technologically literate, (7) ensure that students meet the California Teacher Performance Expectations in mathematics, and (8) ensure that the students meet the California Standards for the Teaching Profession in mathematics.

The course focuses on the teaching and learning of: (1) number concepts including place value and numeration systems, (2) basic facts of the four fundamental operations, (3) whole number computational algorithms, (4) fractions, meaning, and computational algorithms, (5) decimals and computations with decimals, (6) integers and computation with integers, (7) ratio, proportion, and percent, (8) geometry and measurement, (9) algebraic thinking and the use of exponents, and (10) statistics and probability.

Students in the course do problems-of-the-week (POW's) teach mini-lessons, and complete technology activities in data analysis, graphing, and writing assignments focused on communicating mathematics. They each do ten hours of fieldwork in a K–8 mathematics classroom and develop nine lesson plans based on a topic investigated in the course. Subsequently, they teach one of their created lessons to students in their field-assigned classroom.

Course Design Activities

The collaborative process began in the Fall semester of the 2003–2004 academic year. Activities included a series of meetings between the two faculty members to develop an interdisciplinary-based course, including a syllabus, readings, assignments, and course activities, and then pilot the course during the Spring semester of 2004.

Working together, the mathematics and special education faculty identified topics that all elementary school mathematics teachers need to know when teaching students with disabilities. These included the laws governing the education of students with disabilities, the responsibilities of all teachers for the education of students with disabilities, and the need for differentiated instruction. To develop mathematical pedagogical knowledge (MPCK), faculty agreed that pre-service teachers needed experience developing lesson plans and teaching mini-lessons in classrooms that had included students with disabilities. With MPCK, pre-service teachers would gain greater insight into difficulties students typically experience with particular topics in mathematics and they would be better able to deconstruct math topics into units that students could understand *(Anderson & Kim, 2003)*.

A PowerPoint presentation was developed on the history, definitions, and laws governing education of exceptional children. This was presented during the first week of class. Concurrently the special education faculty member and his or her colleagues developed a series of eight case studies (See Figure 1), each one describing a student with a disability who was included in a general education elementary school classroom.

Case Studies

Maria

Maria is a first-grade student with a language-processing disorder. She has an auditory processing problem that interferes with her ability to listen and follow teacher directions. As a result, she often appears to be daydreaming in class when the teacher is engaged in whole-group direct instruction, and she rarely is able to answer a question posed by the teacher and directed to her. When the teacher presents information in a way that Maria can see what she is supposed to learn or do, Maria is much more likely to understand the concept being presented. Likewise, Maria does better with small-group or individualized instruction and with peer tutors than when taught in large-group sessions.

Manuel

Manuel is a fourth-grade student with visual impairments. He has some vision and can see objects and writing placed within 12 inches of his eyes, provided there is limited glare and the print is dark and large in font size. He has excellent auditory processing skills and has learned to compensate for his visual impairment by relying on what he hears and what he can manipulate with his hands. He is very bright and articulate, and has an excellent auditory memory. He can perform most academic tasks at grade level, provided that instructional input and response requirements are modified to compensate for his visual disability.

Figure 1: Case Studies

Jennifer

Jennifer is a second-grade student who is hearing impaired. She has hearing aids in both ears but also relies heavily on sign language to gain instructional input because her hearing is extremely limited. She has an interpreter present in the general education classroom when she is included during instruction. Jennifer's language skills are delayed because of her disability, and this affects the quality of her speech and vocabulary. She is also delayed in her reading ability, particularly in word attack skills and reading comprehension. She is cognitively normal and capable of demonstrating grade-level skill when proper accommodations are provided in the classroom.

Anthony

Anthony is a sixth-grade student with multiple disabilities. He has little or no control of his muscles or skeletal structure and uses a wheelchair with straps and limb supports to keep him sitting and erect. He has very limited oral communication skills and is difficult to understand when he speaks. He communicates with assistive technology, using a computer and keyboard attached to his wheelchair that contains a speech synthesizer that produces speech in response to Anthony touching keys on his keyboard with a stick operated by his mouth. Anthony is very proficient in communicating with this technology. It is difficult for Anthony to keep his head erect for very long periods of time but he takes in information well both visually and through auditory means and understands what he sees and hears quite well. He is cognitively normal and capable of grade-level work.

Laura

Laura is a third-grade student with a learning disability and is currently functioning at the beginning first-grade level in most academic subjects. She has normal IQ but has difficulty with visual memory and processing of visual information. This is evident in her handwriting, which is not well spaced, lacks good letter formation, and when she writes numbers or copies problems from her math book or from the board. She also has difficulty with fine motor skills. She is a very likeable, well-behaved child in class and is anxious to please her teacher. She listens well, is attentive to instruction, and follows directions very well in class. She is well liked by her peers.

Figure 1: Case Studies (Continued)

Julio

Julio is a third-grade student with a developmental disability. His cognitive functioning is significantly below average, his academic ability is around beginning first-grade level, he has difficulty adapting to changes in his environment (e.g., he performs best when things are consistent and routine), and needs intermittent assistance and support from a paraprofessional or peers in order to function successfully in the general education classroom. He is very social and friendly and is well liked by his classmates, teachers, and others in the school. He and his parents want him to participate in the general education classroom to the maximum extent possible and consider developing friendships and relationships, as well as "normal" role models, to be as important as development of his academic skills. He requires very specific steps, directions, reinforcement, and repeated trials to learn academics but is successful when provided this type of instruction.

Joshua

Joshua is a fourth-grade student who is ADHD. He has a very difficult time focusing in the classroom, as evidenced by his high distractibility, frequent movement, and frequent verbal outbursts. He is frequently off task and therefore has trouble working on assignments for very long periods of time. He is very bright and capable of completing quality academic work when he is able to concentrate and take the time necessary to complete assignments. He takes medication and this helps calm him so that he is able to focus on the instruction and complete assignments in class. He works best in 1:1 settings or in small groups, where there are less distractions.

Michelle

Michelle is a sixth-grade student who is traumatic brain injured. Her injury primarily affects her speech, as evidenced by poor articulation skill and difficulty understanding what she says. In addition, she has trouble learning abstract concepts and ideas. She relies on rote memory, repetition, and information presented in a concrete manner. When instructed in this way, she is able to grasp and learn information she is taught. She can communicate very well through reading and writing. She is very social and gets along well with her peers.

Figure 1: Case Studies

Each case study was matched with a lesson plan topic that corresponded to the case study student's grade level (e.g., Joshua and grade 4 multiplication; Maria and concepts of place value). At the end of each topic presented in the methods class (e.g., multiplication basic facts, fractions, decimals), a class discussion was held on what might be expected of the student in the case study on that topic, given the student's disabilities and background knowledge. The methods students were required to include a section in their lesson plans on the types of accommodations they would provide for the assigned student with a disability. Furthermore, when cooperative groups were assigned to teach a mini-lesson on each topic, they were required to address the student with a disability in their mini-lesson and make appropriate accommodations.

Course Assessment Activities

For the revised course taught during the spring semester of 2004, the following types of assessment were conducted: baseline surveys on course participants' knowledge and perceived capabilities for teaching students with disabilities (administered to all students in the fall of 2003); pre- and post-course surveys on course participants' knowledge and perceived capabilities for teaching students with disabilities (administered in the spring of 2004); and exit interviews held with individuals who had completed either the baseline course (fall of 2003) or the newly designed course (spring of 2004), assessing the degree to which the curriculum content and pedagogy emphasized equally the development of mathematics skills in elementary-age students with disabilities and those without.

In order to gather baseline data for comparison, at the end of the fall semester of 2003 but prior to teaching the experimental course, the knowledge and capability surveys were given to students in the mathematics methods course. The surveys contained seven Likert-type questions. Six of the questions surveyed pre-service teachers' general knowledge of students with disabilities; a seventh question surveyed their perceived teaching capability for instructing students with disabilities in mathematics classrooms. A final question assessed whether they had already taken a one-unit course required of all pre-service teachers covering general topics related to laws and best practices for teaching students with disabilities. A survey is attached to the end of this article.

Results showed that course participants who had completed the revised course, in comparison to the baseline group, expressed greater knowledge and perceived capability for teaching elementary mathematics to students with disabilities. This was true, regardless of whether or not they had taken a one-unit overview course on students with disabilities.

Conclusions

The collaborative effort of the faculty who revised the elementary education mathematics methods course clearly resulted in improved knowledge and perceived capability for teaching students with disabilities in elementary-level general education mathematics classrooms. The data substantiated the fact that an introductory-level course focusing on students with disabilities is not enough to promote this outcome in pre-service teachers. Rather, information on instructional methodology for students with disabilities needs to be integrated with content-based elementary-level mathematics instructional methods in order to effectively promote perceived teaching capability in this population of teachers. The results of this study support the argument that without collaboration and definitive course content changes, it is unlikely that pre-service teachers will develop substantive knowledge and perceived capability for teaching students with disabilities who are included in general education mathematics classrooms at the elementary level. It is not enough to legislate inclusion as a means of promoting greater understanding and acceptance by general education teachers of students with disabilities. Unless fundamental changes are made in the way these teachers are trained at the pre-service level, their knowledge and perceived capability for teaching students with disabilities in the classroom is unlikely to change or improve. The implications of this study for teacher training programs are readily apparent, and it is hoped that faculty in teacher training institutions will take note. Moreover, there are many aspects of the course changes discussed in this article that could readily be adapted for use in in-service situations, such as (1) presenting an overview of IDEA and characteristics of various learners with disabilities likely to be included in general education classrooms, (2) discussing various modifications and accommodations for students with disabilities in mathematics, and (3) utilizing the case studies to do small-group activities, such as developing lesson plans around math topics that address students with disabilities.

Inclusive-based education for students with disabilities is a reality in today's public schools. Elementary education mathematics teachers need to be proficient in their abilities to instruct this population of students alongside their non-disabled peers.

References

Anderson, H., & Kim (2003). A missing piece in elementary school mathematics teacher knowledge base. *Issues in Teacher Education, 12*(2), 17–24.

Lesar, S., Benner, S. M., Habel, J., & Coleman, L. (1997). Preparing general education teachers for inclusive settings: A constructivist teacher education program. *Teacher Education and Special Education, 20*, 204–220.

Miller, S. P., Crehan, K., Babbitt, B., & Pierce, T. (2003). Fraction instruction for students with mathematics disabilities: Comparing two teaching sequences. *Learning Disabilities Research and Practice, 18*(2), 99–111.

Smith, D. D. (2004). Introduction to special education: Teaching in an age of opportunity (5th Ed.). Boston: Allyn and Bacon.

Tomlinson, C. A., Nathanson, R., Baker, S. R., & Tamura, R. (2002) Self-determination: What do special educators know and where do they learn it? *Remedial and Special Education, 23*, 242–247.

U.S. Department of Education (2001). *Twenty-third annual report to congress on the implementation of the Individuals with Disabilities Education Act.* Washington, DC: U.S. Government Printing Office.

Wehmeyer, M. L., Field, S., Doren, B., Jones, B., & Mason, C. (2004). Self-determination and student involvement in standards-based reform. *Exceptional Children, 70*(4), 413–425.

Survey: Teacher's Knowledge on Students with Disabilities After Completing the Course

Please rate your knowledge of the topic of teaching elementary education mathematics to students with disabilities after taking the course. Circle the appropriate number below the item description, using the following rubric.

1 = No knowledge of this topic

2 = Minimal knowledge of this topic

3 = Good knowledge of this topic

4 = Excellent knowledge of this topic

A. Least Restrictive Environment (LRE) and inclusive education for students with disabilities in elementary education mathematics classrooms.

1 2 3 4

B. Various types and categories of children with disabilities and the implications for instruction in elementary education mathematics classrooms.

1 2 3 4

C. The role and responsibility of general and special education teachers at the elementary level in the design and delivery of instruction for students with disabilities in elementary education mathematics classrooms.

1 2 3 4

D. Federal legislation related to the education of children with disabilities and legal requirements for teachers to instruct these students in general education classrooms.

1 2 3 4

E. The concept of differentiated instruction when designing and delivering lessons to students with disabilities in elementary education mathematics classrooms.

1 2 3 4

F. Specific strategies and methods for modifying elementary education mathematics instruction for students with disabilities in elementary education mathematics classrooms.

1 2 3 4

G. Please rate the degree to which you currently (prior to the beginning of the course) feel capable of modifying elementary education mathematics lesson plans and curriculum for meeting the individual instructional needs of a variety of students with disabilities.

1 2 3 4

H. Please write any additional comments below related to your preparation for designing and delivering elementary education mathematics instruction to students with disabilities as a result of taking the course.

Author Biographies

Hal Anderson is Professor of Mathematics Education at California State University, Long Beach. He has an extensive background in teacher training as a faculty member in both the mathematics and the teacher education departments. Dr. Anderson teaches both undergraduate and graduate elementary school mathematics content and methods courses.

Scott Baker is Director of Pacific Institutes for Research in Eugene, Oregon and an adjunct faculty member at the University of Oregon. He specializes in early literacy measurement and instruction in mathematics and reading, primarily with students experiencing academic difficulties, including students with learning disabilities and students who are English-language learners. Dr. Baker is currently Principal Investigator on four federally funded projects addressing assessment or instruction for students with learning disabilities or at-risk for learning difficulties.

Edna F. Basik is Associate Professor of Education at National-Louis University in Illinois where she coordinates mathematics education programs. She has co-authored several books focusing on mathematics instruction for students with special educational needs.

Larry Bradsby has served as Director of Mathematics for the Jefferson County School District, Colorado, and directed the development of elementary and secondary curriculum materials. He is lead author of two books, *Math Rescue* and *Algebra Rescue,* and is a frequent speaker at NCSM and NCTM conferences. Dr. Bradsby is a former president of the National Council of Supervisors of Mathematics.

David Chard is Associate Professor of Special Education at the University of Oregon. His research and teaching interests are in early literacy and mathematics instruction for struggling learners. Currently, Dr. Chard is the principal investigator on two federal research projects focusing on reading comprehension and mathematics instruction in the primary grades. Dr. Chard is a former president of the Division for Research at the Council for Exceptional Children and a member of the International Academy of Research on Learning Disabilities.

Ben Clarke is a Research Associate at Pacific Institutes for Research and a school psychologist for the Springfield School District, Springfield, Oregon. His research interests are in the assessment of early numeracy and effective mathematics instruction. Dr. Clarke is currently the project director on a federal research project to design and field test a kindergarten mathematics curriculum.

Debra Coggins is a mathematics education consultant and professional development leader, co-author of *English Language Learners in the Mathematics Classroom,* and lead writer of *A Mathematics Source Book for Elementary and Middle School Teachers: Key Concepts, Teaching Tips, and Learning Pitfalls.* She is a popular speaker at conferences of educators interested in strategies for supporting ELLs and the use of diagrams when teaching mathematical concepts.

Michael L. Connell is Program Area Chair of Mathematics Education at the University of Houston. Dr. Connell's research is in the area of technology-enabled changes in the teaching and learning of mathematics. He has been awarded the Society for Instructional Technology and Teacher Education's outstanding achievement award for best work in putting theory into practice.

Gary Greene is Professor of Special Education at California State University, Long Beach. Dr. Greene trains special education teachers and master's degree students in special education methods, research, and practice.

Delwyn L. Harnisch is Professor of Educational Psychology in the Department of Teaching, Learning and Teacher Education, College of Education and Human Sciences at the University of Nebraska Lincoln (UNL). Dr. Harnisch is currently PI on the UNL Assessment and Leadership for Learning professional development program. His more than 25 years of professional work has focused on integration of technology into the teaching process. He was editor for the National Council on Measurement in Education and developed and directed the NCME website (ncme.org). He is author of more than 150 research articles and books.

Kimberly Hartweg is Professor of Mathematics in the Department of Mathematics at Western Illinois University. Dr. Hartweg teaches content and methods courses for pre-service and in-service teachers. Dr. Hartweg served as co-editor of the Problem Solver's Department of *Teaching Children Mathematics.*

Barbara Smolenski Hinsberger has been teaching mathematics at Westview Hills Middle School in Willowbrook, Illinois for the past 28 years. She also assists with the Future Problem Solving State Competition.

After earning a master's degree in mathematics education, Barbara continued the study of mathematics and of ways to enhance middle school students' understanding of mathematics.

Richard L. Klein teaches mathematics and science at the Monarch School in Houston, Texas. His studies of how people develop and learn helped him formulate a student-centered teaching philosophy that relies on the Montessori philosophy, and on Neuro-Linguistic Programming (NLP). He has implemented his approach in the Monarch School.

Sherry L. Meier is a faculty member at Illinois State University where she specializes in the teaching and learning of mathematics at the middle school level and directs special programs, including the middle school mathematics specialization program in the Department of Mathematics. Dr. Meier was Principal Investigator on two NSF-funded instructional materials development projects. Her research interests include assessment issues in teacher education, interdisciplinary instruction, and the teaching of problem solving.

Judith Olson is a mathematics researcher in the Curriculum Research & Development Group at the University of Hawaii, with a focus on gender equity and the uses of technology in teaching mathematics. Dr. Olson taught K–12 content and methods courses for pre- and in-service teachers for more than 20 years and guided numerous action research projects. She was editor of the Problem Solver's Department of *Teaching Children Mathematics*, a member of the Board of Directors of *School Science and Mathematics*, and a T^3 National Instructor for Texas Instruments.

Melfried Olson is a mathematics researcher at the Curriculum Research & Development Group at the University of Hawaii. He taught content and methods to pre- and in-service teachers for 30 years. Dr. Olson is co-editor of the Problem Solver's Department of *Teaching Children Mathematics*, president of the Research Council on Mathematic Learning, member of the Board of Directors of *School Science and Mathematics*, and Secretary of Women and Mathematics Education.

Beverly S. Rich is a faculty member at Illinois State University and Director of Undergraduate Programs for the Mathematics Department. Dr. Rich was Principal Investigator on a major NSF-funded teacher preparation initiative project. Her research interests include the teaching and learning of mathematics at the secondary level, technology use, and assessment issues in teacher education.

Mary Swarthout is Professor of Mathematics in the Department of Mathematics & Statistics at Sam Houston State University. Dr. Swarthout has served as co-editor of the Problem Solver's Department of *Teaching Children Mathematics* and is currently working on designing and implementing professional development as a part of the Mathematics for English Language Learners (MELL) initiative of the Texas State University System and the Texas Education Agency.

Kathryn Hehl Tomasiewicz is Director of Special Education for the Hinsdale Community Consolidated School District 181. She served as a middle school special education teacher at Maercker School District 60 for 24 years, during which time she had the opportunity to co-teach a remedial mathematics course with co-author Barbara Hinsberger.

NOTES

NOTES